Plumbing

Hot Water Supply and Heating Systems

F. Hall C.Ed., H.N.C., C.G.F.T.C., R.P., M.N.A.P.T., Dip.C.I.O.B.
First Prize and Silver Medal City and Guilds Plumbing

Plumbing

Hot Water Supply and Heating Systems

Third Edition

Longman
Scientific &
Technical

Longman Scientific & Technical
Longman Group UK Limited
Longman House, Burnt Mill, Harlow,
Essex CM20 2JE, England
and Associated Companies throughout the World

First published 1981
Second edition 1987
Third edition 1994

British Library Cataloguing in Publication Data
A catalogue entry for this title is available from the British Library.

ISBN 0 – 582 – 23406 – 9

Set by 4 in 10/12 Compugraphic Times
Printed in Malaysia by TCP

To Nigel

Contents

Preface

The craftsman plumber requires a knowledge of the installation of gas appliances, oil firing systems, hot water supply and heating systems. During their studies at a Technical College or College of Further Education, the student plumber will follow a course in which the subjects studied prepare the student for the award of the National Vocational Qualification (NVQ) in Plumbing.

The primary aim of this book is to assist the plumbing student in their studies for the award of the NVQ. The text deals with gas and oil supplies, and hot water and heating systems. In this third edition, gas installations, heat loss calculations and unvented hot water systems have been revised.

Gas igniters, purging of gas installations, temporary earthing, condensing gas boilers, 'Combi' heating systems and off-peak Economy 7 electric water heating have been added to the text.

The student plumber should also study the installation of cold water supplies, cold water systems, fire control, sanitary appliances, sanitary accommodation, drainage, soil and waste systems and rainwater disposal systems. These topics are explained in a companion volume, *Plumbing: Cold Water Supplies, Drainage and Sanitation*, written by the same author and published by Longman.

Although the book has been written primarily for the plumbing student and craftsman, Building, Surveying and Architectural students taking a BTEC Diploma or Certificate course will find the book useful in their studies for the Building Services and Equipment Unit.

In preparing the book, constant reference has been made to relevant Regulations and Codes of Practice. Wherever possible, written descriptions have been amplified by illustrations, tables and calculations.

I should like to thank the Publishers, their editorial team and Mr C.R. Bassett for their help, and I should like to give a very special thanks to my late wife for her patience and understanding during the preparation of the book and for typing the original manuscript.

F. Hall, 1994

Chapter 1
Natural Gas, Service and Installation Pipework

Formation of Natural Gas

Throughout the world there occur in certain rock formations accumulations of a complex mixture of hydrocarbons to which the name 'petroleum' has been given and, in its natural state, petroleum can exist in solid, liquid or gaseous form, though all are of the same origin.

Solid or semi-solid petroleum is composed of heavier hydrocarbon compounds. It is usually found at the surface of the earth where the lighter hydrocarbons from liquid petroleum near the surface have escaped to the atmosphere. This type of petroleum is called asphalt, tar, pitch or bitumen, and is used by builders for weathering and water-proofing. A good example of this is the asphalt lake in Trinidad.

Natural liquid petroleum is known as 'crude oil' and consists of liquid hydro-carbons, which occur below the surface of the earth, although it sometimes escapes through fissures to the surface. Crude oil is the raw material for oil refineries where fractional distillation separates off petrol, gas oil, diesel oil and fuel oil, leaving pitch or bitumen as the residue.

Characteristics of Natural Gas

Gaseous petroleum is called 'natural gas' and consists of lighter hydrocarbons, which remain gaseous under the conditions of their occurrence, or become gaseous when they reach the surface. The gas consists of methane, ethane, propane and butane, and usually consists of 90% or more methane. The gas usually occurs below the surface of the earth, although like crude oil it sometimes escapes to the surface and evaporates to the atmosphere.

Commercial deposits of petroleum can exist only if geological conditions are favour-able in the first place for their formation. The world's accumulation originates in the deposition of marine organisms, after death, on the sea bed. These organisms, which include plankton, bacteria and simple plants, accumulate with large quantities of inorganic particles deposited by rivers or through chemical precipitation.

A second possible source of natural gas is deep coal measures, where petroleum can be formed under the action of heat and pressure. Once the hydrocarbons have been formed, commercial quantities can accumulate only if there is a suitable trap in which they can collect. As soon as the reactions produce light hydrocarbons, these begin to move upwards, through the salt water that fills the minute pore space in the rock, and into adjacent formations. If, at this stage, a well were to be sunk into the stratum, production would consist of salt water with traces of oil and gas. If, however, the light hydrocarbons even-tually meet an impermeable layer of rock salt, or shale, then an oil or gas field will be formed (see Fig. 1.1).

1

Fig. 1.1 Formation of natural gas.

These structural traps can also be formed by geological faults, which have the effect of sealing off the reservoir rock, or by salt domes formed by the upward intrusion of salt.

Table 1.1 gives the approximate composition of natural gas and Table 1.2 its characteristics.

Gas Burner

Since natural gas has a very slow burning velocity, there is a tendency for the flame to lift off the burner. When light is applied to a mixture of gas and air, the flame formed at the point of ignition spreads through the mass of gas and air at a definite maximum speed, which is known as the burning velocity of the gas.

A burner designed for a specific gas arranges for the speed of travel of the flame to be about the velocity of the mixture of gas and air issuing from the burner, when the flame has reached an area near the port of the burner. This equilibrium between the two velocities propagates a stable flame continuously. If, however, the burning velocity is very low, the velocity of the air and gas mixture from the burner will only have slowed up

Table 1.1 Approximate Composition of Natural Gas

Constituent	Percentage composition
Methane	93
Ethane	3
Propane	2
Butane	1
Nitrogen	1

Table 1.2 Characteristics of Natural Gas

Gross calorific value	37 MJ/m³
Relative density (air = 1.00)	0.55
Density (approx.)	0.7 kg/m³
Flame velocity	350 mm/s
Air required for complete combustion of 1 m³	9.5 m³
Contains no sulphur, therefore causes less corrosion of appliances	
Contains no carbon monoxide and is therefore nonpoisonous	
May contain dust, so filters may be required	

Fig. 1.2 Non-aerated burner or gas pressure too low.

Fig. 1.3 Correct jet size and gas pressure but no retention flame.

Fig. 1.4 Correct jet size and gas pressure but with retention flame.

Fig. 1.5 Box-type gas burner.

enough to balance the velocity of the flame travel when the mixture has spread out at a point well above the burner port. The flame, therefore, forms with its base well above the port, i.e. the flame lifts off.

Natural gas requires an aerated burner: otherwise the gas will not burn completely and the flame will be floppy and rather smoky. The gas pressure and injector jet have therefore to be such that the correct amount of air for complete combustion is achieved. Figs. 1.2, 1.3 and 1.4 show the results of incorrect and correct flame conditions as described.

The tendency of natural gas flames to lift off the burner may also be prevented by increasing the number of ports and therefore the total flame port area. This type is often called a box-type burner and consists of a perforated sheet-metal burner which allows the speed of the gas/air mixture to be reduced and stabilises the flame (see Fig. 1.5).

Service and Installation Pipework

The pipe connecting the consumer's meter with the gas main is known as a service pipe and it should be laid by the shortest practicable route at right angles to the main, with a gradual fall from the meter to the main. The service pipe may be steel or polyethylene. Steel pipes must be protected from corrosion by wrapping with plastic or derso tape, or hessian impregnated with pitch.

Meter Boxes (Fig. 1.6). Whenever possible,

3

Fig. 1.6　Meter box installation.

the termination of the service pipe should be at an external meter box. Installation time and costs can be reduced by use of this box, which has an external lockable door for meter reading. The box is built into the external leaf of the wall and the service pipe and installation pipework connected to it.

The meter box measures 620 mm by 540 mm and can be painted to match the external paintwork. The external meter box allows the meter to be read without having the inconvenience of making special arrangements for the meter reader or the inconvenience of an estimated account.

Service Pipe Entry Above Ground (Fig. 1.7). If the meter has to be sited inside the building, the gas service pipe may be carried up vertically on the outside wall and pass horizontally through the cavity. A sleeve must be provided where the pipe passes through the wall and after the pipe has been installed both ends of the sleeve should be sealed with cement mortar.

Service Pipe Entry Below Ground. Where construction difficulties preclude the use of

an external meter box or riser, the pipe may be carried horizontally through a solid or suspended floor before rising vertically to the meter.

If the pipe passes through a solid floor, a 100 mm diameter sleeve, not more than 2 m long, extending into a 300 mm square hole in the meter position, should be provided (see Fig. 1.8). The annules between the duct and the service pipe should be sealed with a mastic compound. The square hole in the floor should then be filled with sand and the floor finish carried above it. The space around the sleeve on the external wall should be made good with cement mortar.

A service pipe should be laid under a suspended floor only where the void under the floor is ventilated to the outside and the meter positions is not more than 2 m from the outside wall (see Fig. 1.9).

Service Pipe Entry in Garage. The services may be installed in a garage using either the external meter box or a service entry to an internal meter. Where the meter is fitted in the garage, the length of the services inside the garage should not exceed 2 m.

4

Fig. 1.7 Service pipe entry above ground.

Fig. 1.8 Service pipe below solid floor.

Internal Meters. These should be housed inside a ventilated cupboard, preferably recessed into the wall, and standing about 1.4 m above the floor level. The platform on which the meter stands should be level and the cupboard large enough to permit an air space between the meter and the wall. A main control cock should be situated in the cup-

board and, if fitted with a removable key, this should be fixed in a position with a split pin or grub screw.

Meters should not be fitted:

1. under sinks, draining boards, or in a position where they will become wet,
2. in contact with walls,
3. in corrosive or damp atmospheres,

2.000 maximum

Mastic seal

Pipe hanger

Timber floor

Ventilated void

375 mm minimum

Hardcore

Fig. 1.9   Service pipe below suspended floor.

4. in inaccessible positions,
5. above or near a heating or cooling appliance.

Note: in offices or flats, meters should preferably be located so that the dials can be read through a spyhole in the meter cupboard without the inconvenience of entering the office or flat.

Installation Pipework (Fig. 1.10). The pipework from the meter to the gas appliances is called the installation pipework. Larger diameter pipes are of mild steel, whilst smaller pipes are of copper or brass. Flexible metal pipes are used increasingly for connections to meters and appliances (see Fig. 1.11 and 1.12).

Methods of Installation. It is important to know the exact routing of the pipes to avoid the unnecessary cutting away of joists or the chasing of walls and floors. In general, the pipes should rise steadily from the lowest point and a suitable method is to carry the main installation pipe from the meter and to radiate outwards and upwards from this point. A receiver siphon, tap or plug, placed at the lowest point, will permit the collection and removal of any dust or condensate forming in the pipework.

Points to be observed are as follows.

1. Sharp bends should be avoided.
2. Pipes must never be run inside a cavity or unventilated void space.
3. Pipes should be easily accessible without damage to the structure.
4. Pipes should be of incombustible material and adequately supported.
5. As for service pipes, where an installation pipe passes through a floor or wall, a sleeve should be provided and the space between the sleeve and the pipe filled in.
6. Pipes should not be near to any source of heat or dampness.
7. Each run of pipe should be provided with a means of disconnection for easy replacement.
8. Joints should be of an approved type and jointing compounds used should be noncorrosive and allow easy disconnection.
9. Pipes should not touch other service pipes and should be kept as far away as possible from electrical cables or equipment.
10. Pipes must not be run in bedrooms or bedroom cupboards.

Fig. 1.10 Installation pipework.

Fig. 1.11 Gas meter connections for domestic buildings.

Fig. 1.12   Gas meter connections with by-pass for larger buildings.

High Rise Buildings (Figs. 1.13 and 1.14). The vertical service and installation pipes must only be installed in a protected shaft constructed in accordance with the Building Regulations 1976 Sections E10 and E14.

Alternative methods of constructing the protective shaft include the following.

1.   A continuous shaft ventilated to the outside of the building at top and bottom. In this case, a sleeve is required at each point where a horizontal pipe passes through the wall of the shaft and this sleeve must be fire stopped.

Fig. 1.13   Multi-storey building with continuous shaft.

Fig. 1.14 Multi-storey building with sectional shaft.

2. A shaft that is fire stopped at each floor level. In this case, sleeves are required where the riser passes through the floor at each level and where the horizontal pipe passes through the wall of the shaft. the sleeves must be fire stopped. Ventilation to the outside of the building is required at both low and high level for each section of the shaft. Each branch to the meters should be provided with an expansion joint on the vertical plane and the base of the riser should be supported as shown in Fig. 1.15.

Fig. 1:15 Support for steel riser.

Testing For Soundness (Fig. 1.16)

Whenever new gas installation pipes are installed, either complete systems or additions to existing systems, it is essential that they are tested for soundness before they are covered over or protective coatings applied. The tests are carried out as follows.

(a) New Installations
1. Check that all open ends are closed except one, which is fitted with a T piece having a cock on one branch with a U gauge and pump on the other.
2. Pump air into the pipework until the U gauge shows 300 mm water gauge.
3. Shut the cock and allow 1 min for the air temperature in the pipework to stabilise.
4. Allow a further 2 min and if no pressure drop is registered on the U gauge the system is considered sound.
5. Connect the new installation to the gas supply and pump the air from the pipework by opening the main valve, and test the inlet pipework to the meter by using soapy water on the joints and fittings.

(b) Before connecting an extension to existing pipework, the meter and the existing pipework should be tested as follows.
1. Ensure that the meter and consumer's control have been located to ensure that the whole installation is under test.
2. Turn off all appliances and pilot lights.
3. Turn off the main control valve.
4. Connect the U gauge to the pressure test point on the outlet side of the meter.
5. Open the main control valve until the U gauge registers 200 mm. Adjustment may be made by either releasing gas or pumping air into the pipework.
6. Allow 1 min for the temperature of the air in the pipework to stabilise; leave for a further 2 min and check that the pressure drop does not exceed that shown in Table 1.3, and that there is no smell of gas.

    Note: if there is a smell of gas or the pressure drop exceeds that shown in

Fig. 1.16 Testing for soundness.

the table, the leak should be located using a sense of smell or soapy water test.

7. Rectify any leaks and repeat the test and if necessary purge the system of air.

Table 1.3 is based on an average length of pipework, but where the existing installation pipework is usually long the permissible pressure drop will be lower. On completion of the test, the meter control valve should be opened and all pilot lights relit.

Calculation of Gas Pressure

When measuring gas pressure with a U gauge (manometer), atmospheric pressure is ignored. The SI unit for pressure is known as the kilopascal (kPa) which is equal to a kN/m^2. In order to find the pressure in kPa, the head of water measured in metres is multiplied by 9.81. The bar, which is not an SI unit, is equal to 100 kPa and the millibar (mbar) is one thousandth part of a bar. Therefore

$$1 \text{ mbar} = \frac{100 \text{ kPa}}{1000} = 0.1 \text{ kPa}$$

Example 1.1. Calculate the pressure in mbar when the head of water in a U gauge registers 40 mm. (Note 40 mm = 0.04 m.)

Table 1.3 Maximum Permissible Pressure Drop during Two Minutes Final Test Period for Existing Installations

Type of meter	Pressure drop	
	mm water gauge	mbar (approx.)
U6 (D07)	40	4.0
P1 (D1)	25	2.5
P2 (D2)	15	1.5
P4 (D4)	5	0.5

$$\begin{aligned} \text{Pressure} &= 0.04 \times 9.81 \times 10 \\ &= 3.924 \text{ mbar} \end{aligned}$$

Manometers may be obtained which give a direct reading in millibars instead of millimetres. Other uses of the manometer are as follows.

1. Locating excessive pressure loss due to:
   (a) partial stoppage, by taking working pressures reading along the pipeline (Fig. 1.17): a loss of pressure of 10 mbar from A to C indicates that the obstruction is between B and C because the pressure loss between the other sections of pipework is comparatively small;

Fig. 1.17 Test for partial blockage.

11

(b) inadequate pipe size by comparing the difference in readings between the inlet and outlet pressures.

2. Detecting overloading of a meter. This may be found by taking the difference in readings between the inlet and outlet pressure, which difference should not exceed 1.25 mbar.

3. Adjusting appliances. Since gas appliances are designed to give their best performance at a certain pressure and gas flow rate, those can be checked by means of the manometer in conjuction with the pressure governor on the appliance. After setting the pressure, the gas rate to the appliance can be checked by timing the test dial on the meter with a watch.

4. Checking continuity. The gauge can be attached to various points on the pipeline to see if there is any undue drop in pressure. Note: the Gas Safety Regulations require meter pressure governors to be sealed.

Purging the Installation

After testing the installation for soundness air must be purged from the pipework as follows:

1. ensure that there is good ventilation,
2. turn off the main gas cock and ensure all appliance taps are turned off,

3. do not allow smoking or the operation of electrical switches,
4. turn on the main gas cock and purge all pipes of air commencing with the pipe furthest from the meter,
5. the pipework will be purged of air when the meter test dial has made five revolutions.

Note: If the appliance is fitted with a flame-failure safety device, gas will not pass to the burner, and the burner union must be disconnected or the screw in the test nipple removed before purging such pipework.

Temporary Earth Bonding (Fig. 1.18)

Because a metal gas pipe may act as an earth return it is essential to maintain earth continuity at all times. The Institution of Electrical Engineers Regulations require earth bonding of all metal pipes so any leakage of electricity passes through the pipes safely to earth.

If a meter is to be removed or a piece of pipe removed to receive a tee a temporary earth bond is required. The removal of the meter or pipe breaks the earth continuity which could cause a person to receive a fatal electric shock. An electric spark may also pass across the separated pipes possibly causing a fire or, if there is a gas and air mixture in the room, an explosion.

The temporary earth bond consists of single-core, tough rubber sheathed insulated cable not

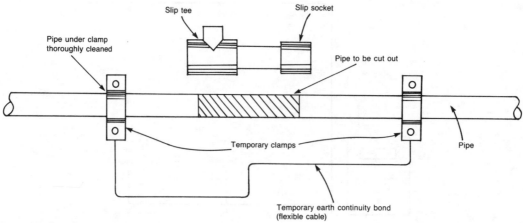

Fig. 1.18 Temporary earth bonding

less than 1.2 m long and having a diameter of 4 mm². The cable should be fitted with an insulated clip or clamp at each end.

The bond must be fitted before the removal of the meter or pipe and the first clamp must be fitted on the upstream side.

Exercises

1. Describe the formation of natural gas.
2. State the main characteristics of natural gas.
3. Sketch and describe the type of burner required for natural gas.
4. Define the following terms:
   (a) burning velocity,
   (b) aerated burner,
   (c) nonaerated burner.
5. Sketch the method of connecting the gas service pipe to the main and state the types of material used for service pipes.
6. Sketch the method of connecting a service pipe to the meter when the meter is sited
   (a) in an external meter box,
   (b) in an internal cupboard.
7. State the safety consideration that must be made when deciding upon the position of a gas meter inside a building.
8. Sketch the method of installing meters and gas riser pipework in high-rise buildings.
9. State the points that must be observed when installing gas pipework in buildings.
10. Sketch and describe the method of carrying out a test for soundness for
    (a) new gas installations,
    (b) existing gas installations.
11. If a U gauge connected to a gas installation shows a reading of 30 mm water gauge, calculate the pressure of gas in the pipework in millibars and pascals.

Chapter 2
Gas Controls

Gas Cocks

The simplest and most common type of control is the gas cock, which is used to shut off the supply of gas to the meter or to individual gas appliances. The cock consists of a tapered plug having a slot through it, which fits into a tapered body. The two connecting surfaces of the plug and tapered body are machined to give a gas-tight seal and these surfaces should be smeared with grease to act as a lubricant. The cock is opened or closed by turning the plug through an angle of 90°. Fig. 2.1 shows a section through a main control cock which incorporates a union to facilitate the removal of the meter.

For safety reasons, a drop-fan cock may be used as shown in Fig. 2.2. The fan is hinged to the plug and has lugs which hold the fan upright when the gas is on. When the cock is turned off, the fan falls and the lugs engage with a slot in the tapered body of the cock. The plug in this off position cannot be turned on until the fan is deliberately held upright and this prevents the cock from being turned on accidentally.

An even safer type of control is known as the plug-in safety cock, shown in Fig. 2.3. This type of cock cannot be turned on without first inserting the outlet pipe to the body of the cock. When the outlet pipe plug is inserted and turned to engage the lugs, two pins on the plug also engage a groove, and a gas-tight seal is made between the two components by compressing the main spring, which forces the two conical surfaces together.

Fig. 2.1 Main control cock.

Fig. 2.2   Drop fan safety cock.

Fig. 2.3   Plug-in safety cock.

Pressure Governor

The control of the gas pressure at the meter or appliances may be achieved by use of a constant pressure governor fitted on the inlet pipe. The governor may be loaded by lead weights or a spring, and the extent of the loading may be adjusted to provide the correct gas pressure at the outlet. A weight-loaded governor must always be in a horizontal position so that the weights act vertically on the diaphragm. Spring-loaded governors, however, may be fixed in any position provided it is easy to adjust the tension on the spring. Fig. 2.4 shows a section through a

spring-loaded governor which operates as follows.

1. Gas enters the governor at the inlet pressure and passes through valve A and also through the space B between the two diaphragms.

2. The main diaphragm is loaded by the spring and the upward and downward forces of gas acting on the diaphragm are balanced. These equal forces have a stablising effect on valve A and prevent any tendency to oscillation.

3. Any fluctuation of inlet pressure will

15

Fig. 2.4 Spring-loaded pressure governor and filter.

inflate or deflate the main diaphragm, thus raising or lowering valve A, altering the resistance to the flow of gas and ensuring a constant pressure at the outlet.

Thermostats

A thermostat is a device that opens or closes a gas valve by sensing the temperature surrounding it. The sensing of the temperature may be achieved by use of the differential expansion of metals, or of the expansion of liquids or vapours when heated.

Rod-Type Thermostat (Fig. 2.5). This type of thermostat may be used for gas-fired boilers, cooker ovens and water heaters.

When the water or air surrounding the brass tube becomes hot, it expands and carries the invar rod (which expands very little) with it. This brings the gas valve closer to its seating, thus reducing or shutting off the flow of gas to the burner. When the water or air cools down, the brass tube contracts, carrying with it the invar rod, thus opening the valve. The bypass permits a small amount of gas to flow when the valve is closed and maintains a small flame at the pilot.

Vapour Expansion Thermostat (Fig. 2.6). These are often used for water heaters and space heaters. The thermostat consists of a capillary tube, probe and bellows, filled with a heat-sensitive vapour such as ether. The thermostatic probe senses the temperature of the water or air surrounding it and the vapour

Fig. 2.5   Rod-type thermostat.

Fig. 2.6   Vapour expansion thermostat.

inside expands. This expansion of the vapour causes the bellows to expand which, in turn, forces the valve A closer to its seating, thus gradually preventing the flow of gas to the burner. When the water or air temperature surrounding the probe lowers, the vapour

contracts, which in turn allows the bellows to contract and valve A to open, thus allowing gas to flow again to the burner.

On/Off Thermostat and Relay Valve (Fig. 2.7). The rod and vapour expansion

Fig. 2.7   On-off thermostat and relay valve.

types of thermostat gradually change the flow of gas to the burner in response to the air or water temperature. The on/off thermostat, as the name implies, immediately allows or stops the flow of gas to the burner.

These types of thermostat are used boilers and warm air heaters, and operate as follows.

1. When the boiler or heater is fired, the gas flows through to the burner because valves A and B are open and the gas pressures above and below diaphragm C are equal.

2. When the water or air reaches the required temperature, the brass casing expands sufficiently to draw valve A, connected to the invar rod, to a closed position. The closing of valve A pre-

vents gas flowing through the weep pipe to the underside of diaphragm C.

3. The gas pressure then builds up above diaphragm C and this allows valve B to fall under its own weight and the flow of gas to the burner is stopped.

4. When the water or air cools down, valve A is again opened, allowing gas to flow to the underside of the diaphragm C, which forces valve B open, and gas is again allowed to flow to the burner.

Note: for valve B to be forced open, the gas above diaphragm C must be removed. This is achieved by a bypass orifice and a weep pipe to the burner, through which the gas escapes and is ignited and burned.

Flame-Failure Devices

It is essential to prevent unburnt gas reaching the burner of an automatic gas appliance in the event of the pilot flame being extinguished. To prevent this possibility and risk of an explosion, a flame-failure device must be fitted.

Mercury Vapour Flame-Failure Device (Fig. 2.8). Mercury is contained in the sensing element, A, which is connected to diaphragm B by a capillary tube. When the sensing element is exposed to the heat of the pilot flame, the mercury vaporises. The resultant pressure of the vapour causes the diaphragm B to expand and this movement is relayed through lever C to valve D, which is forced open and allows gas to flow to the burner.

Should the pilot flame be extinguished, the sensing element A cools and the mercury vapour liquefies, allowing diaphragm B to contract. Spring E then forces valve D down on to its seating, thus preventing the flow of gas to the burner.

Bi-metal Strip Flame-Failure Device (Fig. 2.9). This device consists of two alloys fixed rigidly together and bent into a U shape. The alloys have widely different coefficient of expansion and when the strip is heated, the brass on the outside expands more than the invar on the inside, causing the strip to deflect inwards. This movement opens the gas valve and allows gas to flow to the burner, where it is ignited by the pilot flame.

Should the pilot flame the extinguished, the bi-metal strip cools and deflects outwards, thus closing the gas valve.

Thermoelectric Flame-Failure Device (Fig. 2.10). The sensing element of this device is a thermocouple, which consists of two dissimilar metals joined together to form an electrical circuit. One junction of the two metals is heated by the pilot flame and is known as the 'hot junction' and the other remains relatively cool and is known as the 'cold junction'. When this temperature differential is established, a small electric current is generated and this energy is used to operate an electromagnet in the valve. The electromagnet holds the safety cut-out valve in an open position and allows gas to flow to the burner.

Should the pilot flame be extinguished, the thermocouple is prevented from producing a small current of electricity and the electromagnet is no longer energised. The cut-out valve spring forces the cut-out valve on to its seating and this prevents gas from flowing to the burner.

To light the burner, the following

Fig. 2.8 Mercury vapour flame-failure device.

Fig. 2.9 Bi-metal strip flame-failure device.

procedure is carried out.

1. The gas control cock is opened and the thermostat set at the lowest temperature.

2. The push button is depressed to the full length of its travel. This closes the outlet valve and opens the cut-out valve. At the same time, the plate connected to the safety cut-out valve is forced onto the thermoelectric magnet.

3. The pilot light is ignited by a piezo-electric spark lighter and the thermocouple heated, which energises the electromagnet. It is usually necessary to wait 30 s for the magnet to be energised.

4. The push button is released and the safety cut-out valve is held open by the magnet, which allows gas to flow to the burner and is then ignited by the pilot flame. The temperature setting may now be increased.

Note: if the burner does not light, wait at least 3 min before repeating the above lighting procedure.

Controls Used for Boilers and Heaters

The relative positions of some of the controls already described are shown in Fig. 2.11. These controls are used for boilers or air heaters and are usually sited inside the casing,

Fig. 2.10 Thermoelectric flame-failure device.

Fig. 2.11 Controls used for heaters.

although for clarity they are shown outside in the figure. The constant pressure governor, thermoelectric flame-failure device and relay valve are often combined into one unit.

Thermal Cut-Off Device (Fig. 2.12)

These are used to shut off the supply of gas automatically in the event of fire. When the temperature surrounding the device reaches a temperature of 110 °C, the metal holding a spring-loaded cylinder melts, and the cylinder is forced by the spring onto a seating, closing the valve.

Table 2.1 gives a gas valve fault-finding guide which will be useful when carrying out maintenance work.

The Condensing Gas Boiler

The main difference between a condensing boiler and the standard, non-condensing boiler is that the condensing boiler has a larger heat exchanger. This is achieved by the inclusion of a secondary heat exchanger. The larger heat exchanger surface allows heat to be extracted from the flue gases. In the standard boiler the heat from these gases is discharged through the flue and is lost to the atmosphere.

Fig. 2.12   Thermal cut-off device.

22

In the condensing boiler heat is recovered as the flue gases are cooled from about 250°C to about 50°C. The heat recovered, known as 'sensible heat', improves the boiler efficiency by about seven to eight percentage points.

Natural gas burns in oxygen to produce carbon dioxide and water vapour. The water vapour in a conventional boiler is discharged through the flue with other exhaust gases but in a condensing boiler this water vapour is encouraged to condense hence the name 'condensing boiler'. During condensation the latent heat of vapourisation is recovered and this process further improves the boiler efficiency by about another eight percentage points.

Efficiency   The bench efficiency of a condensing boiler is about 94 to 95 per cent whereas the conventional boiler has a maximum theoretical efficiency of only about 74 per cent.

Gas Igniters

There are two types of gas igniters namely, spark and filament.

Spark igniters   Spark igniters are usually operated by mains electricity. In these igniters an electrical charge is built up in a capacitor until a trigger device allows it to discharge suddenly. The discharge current is stepped up by a transformer to a high voltage of 10 or 15 kV. This spark is strong enough to light the main burner or the gas of a pilot jet. After each spark the capacitor is discharged and the cycle repeated. This type of spark generator can be used to supply a number of burners. Figure 2.13 shows a schematic layout of a mains spark igniter. Spark ignition may also be powered by a battery and so may be used on appliances which have no mains electricity control.

Piezoelectric spark ignition (Fig. 2.14) Such an igniter usually consists of two crystals each 12 mm long and 6 mm in diameter connected in parallel. Applying pressure on the crystals causes a large electrical voltage

Fig. 2.13 Mains spark igniter

When the gas tap is turned on the cam turns anti-clockwise. The lever is depressed and pressure is applied to the crystals. The voltage builds up until it overcomes the spark gap.

Fig. 2.14 Piezoelectric spark ignition

to build up until it overcomes the resistance of the spark gap and sparks are produced. The sparks are of sufficient strength to light the burner of appliances such as gas fires, or the gas of the pilot jet of water heaters and boilers.

Automatic ignition Some appliances have a permanent pilot flame, i.e. the pilot is alight at all times whether or not the main burner is alight. Such appliances have the advantage of cheapness and simplicity but in the interest of economy the pilot flame should be as small as possible. To save gas still further the pilot may be lit automatically by a spark igniter. When the appliance thermostat calls for heat an electric current flows to the spark igniter causing it to create a spark and to light the pilot. Electronic controls also operate an automatic gas valve; it opens to let gas flow to the main burner which is lit by the pilot flame.

The spark gap is usually 3 to 5 mm and the electrodes must not be bent as this may crack the ceramic insulation.

Slow ignition devices　It is essential that the main gas burner should ignite quietly and safely. To ensure this most automatic valves incorporate a slow ignition device which allows the gas valve to open slowly and close quickly. The slow opening ensures a quiet, non-explosive ignition and the quick closing prevents over heating of the water in the boiler or heater.

Filament igniters (Figs 2.15 and 2.16)
Most modern appliances use spark igniters and filament igniters are therefore usually used on older appliances. The igniter consists of an electrically heated filament adjacent to a pilot jet. The filament consists of a small coil of wire which, due to the resistance of the flow of electricity, becomes red-hot and lights the gas on a pilot jet.

The power required for heating the coiled filament may come from either the mains electricity flowing through a step-down transformer or from 1.5 V high power batteries. When a push button switch is depressed electric current flows through the filament.

Manual ignition　This method is only used on old appliances or where the pilot is easily accessible. The pilot is lit by a lighted taper or match.

Fig. 2.15　Mains filament igniter

Fig. 2.16　Battery filament igniter

Exercises

1. Sketch sections and describe the operation of
   (a) a gas cock,
   (b) a drop-fan cock,
   (c) a pressure governor.
2. Sketch and describe the operation of
   (a) a rod-type thermostat,
   (b) a vapour-expansion-type thermostat.
3. Describe the operation of an on/off thermostat and relay valve.
4. Explain the operation of the following types of device
   (a) a mercury vapour flame-failure device,
   (b) a bi-metal strip flame-failure device.
5. Sketch and describe the operation of a thermoelectric flame-failure safety device. Explain the procedure that must be carried out with this type of device in order to light the burner.
6. Sketch an elevation showing the relative positions of the various controls required for gas boilers or gas warm air heaters.
7. Sketch a section through a thermal cut-off device and state its operating temperature.
8. Explain the principle of operation of a condensing gas boiler.
9. Sketch and describe the principles of operation of spark and filament gas igniters.

Table 2.1 Gas Valves — Fault Finding Guide

SYMPTOM

If Glowcoil ignition is fitted, Glowcoil will not light when ignition button is depressed	If spark electrode ignition fitted, no spark when generator energised	Spark at electrode but will not ignite pilot gas	Pilot gas cannot be lighted	Pilot gas can be lighted, but goes out when knob or pushbutton released	Pilot established when knob released, but pilot gas goes out when knob turned to 'ON'	Pilot established, gas cock turned to on, or pushbutton released, but main burner will not fire	Pilot established when knob or pushbutton released, but pilot flame wrong size	Pilot flame cannot be adjusted to correct size	Main burner will fire but pilot flame is immediately extinguished	Pilot established and main burner will fire but system liable to nuisance shutdown	POSSIBLE CAUSE
x											Defective Glowcoil, other ignition comp'nts, fuse, transformer or wiring
x	x										No power supply to ignition circuit
	x	x									Defective spark generator or spark gap too great (see APPLIANCE instructions or set to 3/16" approx.)
		x									Not sparking to inside of pilot target hood
			x								Main service cock (upstream of gas valve) shut off
			x								Gas cock (on valve) in 'OFF' position or latch energised
			x								Gas cock, or pushbutton, not held fully depressed
			x								Pilot gas line not yet purged of air
			x								Pilot filter blocked
			x								Pilot gasways blocked
			x								Pilot gas adjuster closed too far
			x								Pilot gas line blocked
			x								Pilot burner orifice blocked
				x							Gas cock or pushbutton released too soon
				x						x	Dirty or loose thermocouple connection
				x					x	x	Wrong size pilot flame
				x						x	Defective thermocouple
				x						x	Defective Pilotstat
					x						Excessive grease in gas cock (plug and seating) blocking pilot gasway when turned
						x					External controls (Clock, boiler thermostat, etc.) not calling for heat
						x					Defective fuse, transformer or power supply
						x					Defective external controls or wiring
						x					Governor stuck in closed position
						x					Operator open circuited (test for voltage at Operator terminals)
							x		x		Pilot gas adjuster screw set incorrectly
								x	x		Incorrect pilot orifice fitted for type of gas used
									x		Gas supply too small or restricted
											Short circuit in external controls or wiring
											Defective Operator
											Defective governor
											Governor spring requires adjustment
											Wrong governor spring fitted for pressure range required
											Loose screws at joint
											Defective gasket
											Damaged casting at joint
											Calibration needs adjustment
											Wrong Modusnap operator for application
											Defective thermostat (if room thermostat, it may need calibrating)
											Poor location for room thermostat
											Wrong low fire orifice fitted or incorrect adjustment
											Leak at pressure regulator or Operator gasket

Main gas will not shut down in response to external controls	Gas valve noisy when main burner is firing	Main burner pressure cannot be maintained at constant level	Main burner pressure incorrect	Gas leaks from joint at gas valve body/governor/Pilotstat/operator on soap solution check	(V5130 only) Correct temperature settings cannot be obtained	(Modusnap valves only) Correct temperature settings cannot be obtained	(Electric Operator valves only) Correct temperature settings cannot be obtained	(Modusnap valves only) Low fire gas rate incorrect	(Modusnap valves only) Valve will not shut down when heat demand falls below low fire rate	(Servo-series valves only) Electrical power at Operator terminals but valves will not open	POSSIBLE CAUSE
											Defective Glowcoil, other ignition comp'nts, fuse, transformer or wiring
											No power supply to ignition circuit
											Defective spark generator or spark gap too great (see APPLIANCE instructions or set to 3/16" approx.)
											Not sparking to inside of pilot target hood
											Main service cock (upstream of gas valve) shut off
											Gas cock (on valve) in "OFF" position or latch energised
											Gas cock, or pushbutton, not held fully depressed
											Pilot gas line not yet purged of air
											Pilot filter blocked
											Pilot gasways blocked
											Pilot gas adjuster closed too far
											Pilot gas line blocked
											Pilot burner orifice blocked
											Gas cock or pushbutton released too soon
											Dirty or loose thermocouple connection
											Wrong size pilot flame
											Defective thermocouple
											Defective Pilotstat
											Excessive grease in gas cock (plug and seating) blocking pilot gasway when turned
											Extenal controls (clock, boiler thermostat, etc.) not calling for heat)
											Defective fuse, transformer or power supply
											Defective external controls or wiring
											Governor stuck in closed position
											Operator open circuited (test for voltage at Operator terminals)
											Pilot gas adjuster screw set incorrectly
											Incorrect pilot orifice fitted for type of gas used
											Gas supply too small or restricted
X											Short circuit in external controls or wiring
X	X								X		Defective Operator
		X									Defective governor
			X								Governor spring requires adjustment
			X								Wrong governor spring fitted for pressure range required
				X							Loose screws at joint
				X							Defective gasket
				X							Damaged casting at joint
					X	X					Calibration needs adjustment
						X					Wrong Modusnap operator for application
							X				Defective thermostat (if room thermostat, it may need calibrating)
							X				Poor location for room thermostat
								X			Wrong low fire orifice fitted, or incorrect adjustment
										X	Leak at pressure regulator or Operator gasket

Chapter 3
Gas Flues and Fires

Definitions

The following are common definitions applicable to gas flues and fires.

APPLIANCE: a heat producing appliance (including a cooker) designed to burn gaseous fuels.

APPLIANCE VENTILATION DUCT: a duct forming a passage which in one part serves to convey combustion air to one or more gas appliances, in another part serves to convey the products of combustion from one or more gas appliances to the external air and intermediately serves both purposes.

BRANCH (SHUNT) FLUE SYSTEM: a flue system comprising a common main flue into which more than one conventionally flued appliance may discharge on each or several floors in a medium-rise or multi-storey building.

CHIMNEY: includes any part of the structure of a building forming part of a flue other than a flue pipe.

HEAT INPUT: in relation to a gas appliance, means the gas consumption of the appliance expressed in terms of the quantity of heat supplied to the appliance in a specific time.

DISCHARGE: the discharge of the products of combustion.

FLUE: a passage for conveying the discharge of an appliance to the external air, including any part of the passage in an appliance ventilation duct which serves the purpose of a flue.

GAS FIRE: a flued appliance for heating one room, mainly by the emission of radiant heat, and not comprising any water-heating component.

HIGH-RATING APPLIANCE: a gas appliance having an input rating exceeding 45 kW, or an incinerator having a refuse combustion chamber exceeding 0.08 m³ in volume.

INSULATED METAL CHIMNEY: a chimney comprising a flue lining, noncombustible thermal insulation, and a metal outer casing.

MAIN FLUE: a flue serving one appliance.

PERMANENT VENT: a purpose-made opening or duct designed to allow the passage of air at all times.

ROOM-SEALED APPLIANCE: a gas appliance that draws in combustion air from a point immediately adjacent to a point where it discharges its products of combustion and is so designed that the inlet, outlet and combustion chamber of the appliance, when installed, are isolated from the room or internal space in which the appliance is situated, except for a door for ignition purposes.

SUBSIDIARY FLUE: a flue conveying the discharge of an appliance into a main flue.

TERMINAL: a device, fitted at the termination of the chimney or flue, designed to allow free egress of the products of combustion, to minimise down draught and to prevent the entrance of foreign matter which may cause restriction of the flue.

VENTILATION OPENING: any openable part of a window or hinged panel, adjustable louvre or other means of ventilation that opens directly into the external air, but excluding any opening associated with mechanically operated systems.

Sizes of Gas Flues
(open-flued appliances)

The Building Regulations 1992 give the following sizes of flues:

1. no dimension should be less than 63 mm, or
2. flues for decorative appliances, i.e. log and other solid fuel fire effect gas appliances, should have no dimension across the axis less than 175 mm, or
3. flues for gas fires should have a cross-

sectional area of at least 12 000 mm²
and if the flue is rectangular, the greater
dimension should not be more than six
times the lesser, or

4. any other appliance should have a flue
with a cross-sectional area at least equal
to the size of the outlet from the appliance and if the flue is rectangular, the
greater dimension should not be more
than five times the lesser.

Materials used for Flue Pipes

The Building Regulations 1992 specify the
following

1. sheet metal as described in BS 715 :
1970, 'Sheet metal flue pipes and accessories for gas fired appliances', or
2. stainless steel, or
3. asbestos cement as described in BS 567 :
1973 (1984), 'Asbestos-cement flue
pipes and fittings, light quality', or
4. cast iron as described in BS 41 : 1973
(1981), 'Cast iron spigot and socket flue
or smoke pipes and fittings', or
5. flue blocks as described in BS 1289 :
1975, 'Precast concrete flue blocks for
domestic gas appliances'.

A chimney may be built of any masonry
material with a lining or of flue blocks
without a lining. Linings may be of one of the
following:

1. clay flue liner with rebated or socketed
joints as described in BS 1181 : 1971
(1977), 'Clay flue linings and flue
terminals',
2. imperforate clay flue pipes as described
in BS 65 : 1981, 'Specification for
vitrified clay pipes fittings and joints',
3. a flexible flue liner may be used in a
chimney if:
   (a) the liner complies with the requirements of BS 715 : 1970 sheet
   metal flue pipes and accessories for
   gas fired appliances, and
   (b) the chimney was built before 1
   February 1966.

Note: Flue pipes with spigot and socket joints
should be fitted with sockets uppermost and
flue linings should be fitted with the sockets

or rebates uppermost to prevent condensate
running out and to prevent any caulking
material from being adversely affected.
Joints between the liners and masonry should
be fitted with mortar. Factory-made insulated chimneys may also be used.

Outlets from Flues

The outlet should be:

1. so situated externally that air may pass
freely across it at all times, and
2. at least 600 mm from any opening into
the building, and
3. fitted with a flue terminal where any
dimension across the axis of the flue
outlet is less than 200 mm.

Openings into Flues

No opening should be made in a flue except
for:

1. inspection or cleaning, when the opening should be fitted with a noncombustible gas-tight cover, or
2. a draught diverter.

Communication Between Flues

No flue should have openings to more than
one room or space except for an opening for
inspection or cleaning.

Purposes of Flues

Gas flues in a building provide two main
functions, to

1. remove the products of combustion
from the appliance to the atmosphere,
2. assist in providing ventilation of the
room where the appliance is installed.

Design Factors

The decisive requirements for a flue are:

1. gas rate per hour used by the
appliance,
2. volume of room and the standard of
ventilation,
3. period of continual use of the room.

If roof pitch is less than 45° A
must be 600 mm minimum. If
roof pitch is 45° or over A
must be 1 m minimum.

Terminal

A

Precast concrete
flue 25 mm thick
minimum

Secondary
flue

Gas fire
starter blocks

Sockets facing
upwards

Socket facing upwards

135°

600 mm minimum

Copper
condensation
pipe

Draught diverter

Primary flue

Appliance

Fig. 3.1 Open gas flues.

Types of Gas Flue

There are two types of flue.
1. Open (see Fig. 3.1), which consists of
   (i) a primary flue, which determines the speed at which the products of combustion leave the appliance,

(a) During normal operation

(b) During down draught

Fig. 3.2   Operation of draught diverter.

(ii) a draught diverter, which, as the name implies, diverts down-draught during adverse wind conditions, and also dilutes the products of combustion and prevents excessive draught on the burner (Fig. 3.2 shows the operation of the draught diverter),

(iii) a secondary flue, which is the flue proper and carries the products of combustion to a suitable position where they can be released to the atmosphere: it should be kept as short as possible and changes of direction should be reduced to the minimum, and

(iv) a terminal, the purpose of which is to prevent the entry of birds, rain and wind into the flue: it should have a free area equal to at least twice the cross-sectional area of the flue.

2. Balanced (see Fig. 3.3), which is a room-sealed appliance designed to draw in the air required for combustion from a point immediately adjacent to where it discharges its products of combustion. A balanced flue has the advantages over the conventional flue that

   (i) it has a higher efficiency due to less heat loss from the flue,
   (ii) it has no need for an expensive long flue,
   (iii) it is neater and cheaper,
   (iv) the appliance may be fitted in a confined space,
   (v) there is less risk of condensation, and
   (vi) there is less risk of the products of combustion entering the room.

   Its disadvantages are that
   (i) the appliance can be fitted only on an outside wall, and
   (ii) the terminal position may present some problems.

Table 3.1 gives the positions of balanced flue terminals which should be read in conjunction with Fig. 3.4.

31

Convected heat

Terminal

Products of combustion

Combustion air

Burner

Fig. 3.3 Balanced flue convector heater.

Gutter

Gutter

F BCD

BCD

Soil and vent pipe

Openable window

Openable window

A

H E E

F

F F

A

G

Rainwater pipe

Fig. 3.4 Positions of balanced flue terminals.

Table 3.1 Terminal Positions for Balanced Flue Appliances

Note: if a terminal is fitted within 850 mm of a plastic or painted gutter or 450 mm of a painted eaves, an aluminium shield, at least 750 mm long should be fitted to the underside of the gutter or painted surface.

Terminal position	Minimum distance	
	Natural draught (mm)	Forced draught (mm)
A Directly below an openable window or any other opening, e.g. air brick	300	300
B Bellow gutters soil or drain pipes	300	75
C Below eaves	300	200
D Below balconies	600	200
E From soil or vent pipes	600	75
F From internal or external corners	600	300
G Above ground or balcony level	300	300
H From a surface facing the terminal	600	600
I From a terminal facing another terminal	600	1200

Operation of the Balanced Flue

Because the air inlet and flue outlet are adjacent, any variations of wind pressure has an equal effect on each, and the air pressure inside the appliance is not affected. The column of cool air from outside displaces the column of hot gases inside the appliance.

Flue Routes

A gas flue should take the most direct route and its rise should be continuous towards the terminal. Horizontal runs should be avoided since they impede the flow of gases and cause local cooling. A vertical route between the secondary flue and the flue pipe passing through the wall to atmosphere is essential, for it is at this point that the flue gases are at the highest temperature and are able to provide the greatest motive force.

A flue should be sited inside the building as far as is practical. An internal flue will keep the heat losses down to a minimum and help to reduce condensation.

Fire Precautions

The basic requirements for fire precautions is that the temperature of any combustible material in the vicinity of a flue should not exceed 65 °C and no flue should be nearer than 50 mm from combustible material.

Where a flue pipe passes through a combustible roof, floor, ceiling or partition, the pipe should be enclosed in a imperforate, noncombustible sleeve, the diameter of which should be sufficient to provide an annular space of not less than 50 mm between the flue pipe and the sleeve (see Fig. 3.5).

If a flue pipe passes through a room, or enclosed space, other than that in which a gas appliance is fitted, any part of the flue pipe which might reach 90 °C should be protected to prevent contact with it by persons using the room.

Where a flue pipe passes through a room other than that in which a gas appliance is fitted, no joints connecting the flue pipe must be in that room.

Termination of Flues

In order to prevent excessive down draught, it is essential that the terminal of a flue is kept out of high-pressure regions. High-pressure regions may occur in the corners of buildings, below the eaves or parapet walls, or close to vertical pipes.

Where a flue pipe passes through a flat roof and the pipe is within 1.5 m of a parapet wall, measured horizontally, the pipe should be

Non-combustible material

Metal sleeve

Timber floor

Airspace

Metal flange

Flue pipe

Fig. 3.5 Flue pipe passing through a timber floor or ceiling. A = 50 mm minimum, B = 25 mm minimum.

carried up at least 600 mm above the top of the wall (see Fig. 3.6).

If a flue pipe passes through a flat roof not having a parapet wall, the pipe should be

carried up at least 600 mm above the roof (see Fig. 3.7).

If a flue pipe passes through a flat roof, with or without a parapet wall, the outlet

A must be not less than 600 mm unless B is greater than 10 × C in which case A must not be less than 250 mm

600 mm minimum

Within 1.500

A

B

C

Fig. 3.6 Flat roof with parapet wall.

34

Fig. 3.7 Flat roof without parapet wall.

should not be below a level corresponding to the height of any part of the structure that is at a distance exceeding 1.5 m, measured horizontally, from the outlet reduced by one third of the difference between such distance and 1.5 m (see Fig. 3.8).

The outlet should also be sited at least 600 mm from any window, skylight ventilator or air inlet to a ventilating system if these are capable of being opened and are in any roof or external wall.

If the appliance is an incinerator, the flue outlet should not be less than 1 m above the top of any opening situated less than 2.3 m, measured horizontally, from the outlet.

Ventilation Requirements

An adequate supply of air is essential for the satisfactory operation of gas appliances. The Building Regulations do not require an air vent to a room or space in which a balanced flue appliance is installed.

Where a balanced flue appliance is installed in a compartment, however, it is good practice to provide ventilation to the space for cooling purposes. The cooling air may be from the room through vents in the compartment door or from the outside through vents in the outside wall. The air vent should be direct to the external air, or to an adjacent room or internal space that itself has an air vent to the external air. Fig. 3.9 shows the methods of providing vents to a gas appliance.

Compartment Ventilation (Fig. 3.10)

A boiler compartment is a totally enclosed space within a building, either constructed or modified specifically to accommodate a boiler and its ancillary equipment, excluding

Fig. 3.8 Flat roof with a structure near the terminal, A = $(x - 1.5 \text{ m})/3$. Therefore, if x = 3 m then A = (3 m − 1.5 m)/3 = 0.5 m = 500 mm (maximum)

Fig. 3.9 Ventilation of gas appliances.

a gas meter. The requirements for a boiler compartment are as follows.

1. It should be a fixed rigid structure.
2. It should incorporate adequate air vents.
3. It should be fitted with a door of sufficient size to permit the removal of the boiler and ancillary equipment.
4. It should be of sufficient size to permit access for inspection and servicing. It should, however, not be too large or it may be used as a storage cupboard.

Fig. 3.10 Methods of providing vents to gas appliances fixed inside a compartment.

5. Where the compartment houses an open-flued appliance, neither the door nor the vents should communicate with a bedroom, bed-sitting room or space containing a bath or shower.
6. Any combustible material should be at least 75 mm from any part of the boiler. Alternatively, it should be lined with noncombustible material or treated with a suitable fire-retarding paint.

Table 3.2 gives the minimum effective area requirements for compartment permanent air vents for open-flued and room-sealed appliances. Table 3.3 gives the Building Regulations 1992 on minimum unobstructed area of permanent vents to gas appliances.

Adventitious Ventilation

Adventitious ventilation is air that can enter a room through cracks around doors and openable windows, etc. Tests have shown that even after weather stripping and double glazing it is virtually impossible to restrict the area of these openings to the room to less than the equivalent of an air vent having an effective area of 3500 mm².

An allowance for adventitious openings of 3500 mm² can therefore safely by made for open-flued appliances, because the air flow in the flue will draw air into the room through these openings.

Table 3.2   Minimum Effective Area Requirements for Compartment Permanent Air Vents (British Gas)

Permanent air vent position	In a compartment ventilated to a room or internal space (mm²/kW)	In a compartment ventilated to the outside (mm²/kW)
(a) *Open-Flued appliances*		
High-level	900	450
Low-level	1800	900
(b) *Room-sealed appliances*		
High-level	900	450
Low-level	900	450

Table 3.3   Minimum Unobstructed Area of Permanent Vent

Type of appliance	Volume of room or power output of appliance	Minimum unobstructed area of vent to outside air
Cooker	1. volume of room 6 m³ minimum, and	
	2. an openable window or other opening to the outside air, and	
	3. vent area for a room volume less than 9 m³, and	6500 mm²
	4. vent area for a room volume between 9 m³ and 11 m³	3500 mm²
Open-flued (decorative)	vent area for each kW of rated input over 2 kW	1800 mm²
Any other open-flued	vent area for each kW of rated input over 7 kW	450 mm²

Notes: decorative appliances are decorative log and other solid fuel fire effect gas appliances. Extract fans could affect open-flued appliances.

If the room contains two or more appliances, the total air vent requirement is the largest of the following:

1. the total flueless space-heating appliance requirement,
2. the total open-flued space-heating appliance requirement,
3. the largest individual requirement of any other type of appliance.

Location of Air Vent

Where an air vent is fitted in an internal wall, it should not communicate with a bedroom, toilet, bathroom or kitchen. It should be located not more than 450 mm above the floor level, in order to reduce the spread of smoke in the event of a fire. An air vent direct to the outside must not be positioned less than 600 mm away from any part of an open-flue terminal, nor less than 300 mm directly above any part of a balanced flue terminal. An air vent across a cavity wall must include a continuous duct across the cavity. Note: existing or new air vents should be regularly examined to check that they are not obstructed.

Terminals

The outlet of any flue serving a gas appliance must be fitted with a terminal designed to allow free discharge of the products of combustion, minimise downdraught and prevent the entry of any matter that might restrict the flue. Figs. 3.11 and 3.12 show the types of terminal that are fixed to a vertical flue pipe that passes above the roof.

Fig. 3.13 shows the type of terminal that may be used when the flue pipe passes vertically to the outside. These three different types of terminal are designed to resist the effect of wind pressure, which might cause downdraught in the flue.

Fig. 3.14 shows a stainless steel ridge terminal, and a similar type of terminal may be obtained manufactured from clay. There is normally no high-pressure region at the ridge and therefore this is usually the best possible position for a flue terminal.

Plan

Fig. 3.11   GLC terminal.

Louvres

Fig. 3.12   GCI terminal.

Wind

Plan

Fig. 3.13   'Denham' terminal for vertical fitting.

39

Fig. 3.14   Stainless steel ridge terminal.

Shared Flues

The shared flue system is suitable for high-rise buildings and reduces the cost and space that would be required if separate flues for each appliance were used. There are three systems.

1. Se-duct (Fig. 3.15). Room-sealed appliances may be connected on each side of the flue. The air required for combustion is drawn in from the base of the duct and the entry of this air depends on the type of building structure. If required, a horizontal flue above or below ground level may be used: if the building is built on columns, the horizontal flue is not required.

2. U duct (Fig. 3.16). This type of duct offers an alternative to the Se-duct system in cases where there are difficulties in arranging the air supply at the bottom of the duct. The U duct requires two vertical ducts; the downflow duct draws air from the roof-level inlet. The room sealed appliances are connected to the upflow duct only.

3. Shunt duct (Fig. 3.17). This type is designed for the flueing of conventional appliances. The system consists

Fig. 3.15   Se-duct system.

40

Products of combustion

Combustion air inlet

Water heater →

Air heater →

Fig. 3.16   U-duct system.

of a main flue with subsidiary flues connected to it by means of a 2 m vertical shunt. The system allows assistance in ventilating the room in which the appliance is installed.

Table 3.4 gives the number of appliances that may be connected to flues.

Balanced-flued Appliances (terminals)

The Building Regulations 1992 state that balanced-flued appliances should be installed so that the appliance terminal is:

1. so situated externally as to allow free intake of air and disposal of products of combustion, and
2. at least 300 mm from any opening into the building which is wholly or partly above the terminal, and
3. protected with a terminal guard if it could come into contact with people near the building or be subejct to damage, and
4. designed so as to prevent the entry of

any matter which might restrict the flue.

Note: The Building Regulations 1992 state that if the gas appliance is in a bath or shower room or a private garage it must be a balanced-flue appliance.

Gas Fires

The installation of a gas fire is generally one of the less difficult tasks that the installer has to carry out. Reports of incidents involving gas fires, however, have shown that hazardous conditions may result from unsatisfactory installation, by not taking into account certain precautions recommended by the manufacturer. It will be necessary to establish whether the selected fire is suitable for the type of flue into which it is to be fitted. Some gas fires are not suitable when connected to a precast concrete flue.

Having selected the right type of fire for the situation, the following checks on the flue

Fig. 3.17 Shunt duct system.

Table 3.4 Appliances Discharging by way of Subsidiary Flues into a main flue

	Nominal cross-sectional area of main flue			
	Not less than 40 000 mm² but less than 62 000 mm²		62 000 mm² or more	
	Maximum number of appliances	Total rating in kW	Maximum number of appliances	Total rating in kW
Convector fire with controlled flue flow having a maximum rate of flow of 70 m³/h	5	30	7	45
Instantaneous water heater	10	300	10	450
Storage water heater, central heating unit or air heater	10	120	10	180

should be made.

1. The flue must be clear of soot and, if a solid fuel fire has been in use, it is essential to have the chimney swept.
2. The flue must not connect with another flue and the route of the flue must be examined to establish that only one room is served by the flue.
3. The flue must not be blocked by rubble, sheets of newpaper or restrictor plate.

Most gas fires have an integral tap, but to facilitate servicing of the appliance a separate tap should be fitted close to the appliance.

Back Boilers. Back boilers may be used for central heating and hot water supply. These are set in the fireplace opening behind the gas fire. The back boiler and the fire are entirely independent, working together or separately as required. The system is very economical, as the fire itself is not needed for water heating. The boiler is thermostatically controlled so that it operates economically. Fig. 3.18 shows the installation of a gas fire incorporating a back boiler.

The following checks should be made.

1. The vertical height between the gas burner and the finished floor level or floor covering should not be less than 225 mm.
2. The hearth of noncombustible material must extend at least 300 mm from back to front and at least 150 mm sideways beyond the edge of the radiant source.
3. Any part of the rear of the appliance where the temperature is likely to

Fig. 3.18   Combined gas fire and back boiler.

exceed 65 °C, should be separated from any combustible material by an air gap of at least 76 mm.

4. Any combustible side wall less than 500 mm from the radiant heat source must be suitably protected.

5. Any electrical wiring and equipment must comply with the IEE Regulations for the electrical installations in buildings and also with the requirements of CP 321.

6. The gas pressure should be checked and adjusted with the manufacturer's instructions.

Exercises

1. Define
   (a) appliance ventilating duct,
   (b) room-sealed appliance,
   (c) subsidiary flue,
   (d) primary and secondary flues.

2. State the types of material that may be used for gas flues and compare the advantages of each.

3. State the purposes of flues and the factors governing their design.

4. Sketch a conventional type of gas flue for a gas water heater showing all the components.

5. Sketch a section through a draught diverter and explain its operation.

6. Sketch a section through a balanced flue appliance, explain its operation and state its advantages over a conventional type of flued appliance.

7. State the considerations that must be taken into account for
   (a) routes for flues,
   (b) fire precautions for flues.

8. State the positions required for flue terminals and explain the reasons for using these positions.

9. Explain the requirements for the ventilation of gas appliances including 'compartment ventilation'.

10. Sketch a flue terminal for a position
    (a) where a flue pipe passes through a roof,
    (b) where a flue pipe passes to a ridge,
    (c) where a flue pipe passes through a wall.

11. Sketch vertical sections and explain the operation of the following types of shared flue:
    (a) Se-duct,
    (b) U duct,
    (c) shunt duct.

12. State the requirements of the Building Regulations 1992 for the connections of room-sealed appliances to shared flues.

13. Sketch and describe the method of installing a gas fire and state the checks that must be made before and after installing the fire.

Chapter 4
Oil Firing, Calorific Values

Oil Burners

Because oil fuel in bulk will not burn easily, it is necessary to provide some means by which small quantities can be vapourised or atomised and mixed with air in the correct ratio to form a combustible mixture, which can then be ignited and burned to release heat. There are two types of oil burner: vaporising and atomising.

Vaporising Oil Burners

These are by far the most commonly used type in domestic heaters and are almost silent in operation. They can be installed in a kitchen or living room. There are three classes of vaporising burner: (a) rotary vaporising burner, (b) natural draught pot vaporising burner and (c) forced draught pot burner.

Rotary vaporising burners. These are fully automatic burners suitable for heaters providing 12–44 kW. The burner is entirely dependent on a mains electrical supply and a flue capable of providing a steady draught of about 5 Pa. There are two forms of this type of burner, namely Wallflame and Dynaflame burners.

Wallflame burners (Fig. 4.1) consist of a steel plate securing a centrally placed electric motor. The armature of this motor is wound on a hollow metal shroud and is termed the rotor. The bottom of the shroud dips into an oil well, which also supports the trust bearings of the rotor spindle.

A constant-level oil control feeds oil into the well and maintains it at a level just covering the edge of the shroud. The shroud is circular, with its internal diameter increasing towards the top, from which two holes connect with a pair of oil distributor pipes, which are inclined outwards and project through the base of the plate.

Above these tubes and mounted on the rotor spindle is an air fan, and on top of the steel plate there is a ciccular refractory hearth. Within the circumference of the hearth there is a sheet metal band arranged so as to provide an air gap to insulate the lower part of the boiler from the burner flame. Fixed on the hearth, concentric with the backing band, is a trough-shaped flame rim on which is mounted a number of grilles.

A high-tension electrode is fitted into the base of the hearth and projects into the flame rim trough. On some models of this type of burner, flame rim heating is also provided to assist in flame ignition.

The burner is controlled in accordance with demands for heat and therefore operates on the on/off sequence. As soon as the burner is switched on, a high-tension electric arc is established between the electrode and the flame rim. On models incorporating a rim heater, the start-up sequence begins with this heater being energised. The motor drives the rotor clockwise and oil is lifted through the shroud and oil distribution tubes by cen-

Fig. 4.1 Wallflame rotary vaporising burner.

trifugal force and ejected as a horizontal spray onto the flame rim. The droplets of oil that fall on the hot spot on the rim, created by the high-tension spark, vaporise rapidly and are ignited by the spark.

Heat is radiated from the burning vapour and flame is quickly established around the complete circumference of the hearth. The grilles on top of the flame rim shortly become red hot and radiate heat down onto the oil to cause it to vaporise almost instantaneously. When the burner is firing correctly, the flame burns through the grilles providing a wall of flame around the circumference, hence the name 'wallflame'.

Air for combustion is drawn through the hollow air casing of the motor and is projected horizontally across the hearth by the fan. An air shutter provides for regulation of the volume of combustion air as required.

Dynaflame burners (Fig. 4.2) have many unique features. Exclusive to this burner are a constant-output fuel-metering system, which

ensures that the correct amount of fuel is always available, and a controlled recirculation of gases resulting in a blue flame combustion. Operation is controlled from a special control box and ignition power pack.

The burner consists of two main parts: (a) the casing assembly and (b) the rotary assembly. The casing assembly is attached to the boiler by engaging the slotted holes into fixing bolts in the boiler base plate. The assembly contains the stator of the high-speed burner motor, a central fuel reservoir and an adjustable combustion air shutter.

The mounting flange contains a fixed airway to allow air to flow into the combustion chamber and also houses an ignition plug, ignition ring and flame detector. A vertical fuel-metering column and external helical grooving is mounted within the base of the fuel reservoir, and this also provides a bearing for the rotating assembly.

The rotating assembly comprises a central tube, with internal sleeve and bearing, and a

Labels on figure:
- Fan assembly
- Motor rotor
- Ignition ring
- Motor stator
- Flame detector
- Fuel metering stem and bearing pad
- Igniter
- Motor
- Air supply regulator

Fig. 4.2   Dynaflame rotary vaporising burner.

double-tiered fan assembly attached to its upper end by means of an internal cone. The rotor of the burner motor is attached around the tube.

A flame stabiliser, which is fitted around the base of the combustion chamber in the boiler and above the burner, assists in achieving a stable flame pattern. The oil is supplied to the burner via a constant-level oil control device.

The boiler thermostat controls the start and stop operation of the burner, unless this is overidden by a time control, programmer or frost thermostat.

When the electrical supply is switched on, a minimum of 95 s elapses before the thermostat can start the burner. When the thermostat initiates the starting cycle, the igniter is connected to the electrical supply and reaches

ignition temperature within 25 s. A changeover switch in the ignition circuit then operates to start the burner motor and the rotating assembly runs at full speed.

A metered quantity of oil is lifted up a spiral passageway between the rotating tube and the fuel-metering column and passes inward and upwards through holes at the top of the metering column, entering the base of a hollow fuel-discharge cone. The rotating effect lifts the fuel uniformly to the uppermost edge of the cone and discharges it from the edge of the upper flange, in the form of fine particles, into the blades of the surrounding top fan assembly.

Air is drawn through the fan from the combustion chamber, mixes with the oil and this fuel passes over the hot igniter. Local ignition occurs immediately and a full circle of flame is quickly established in the ignition ring, which surrounds the fan. Combustion air supplied by the lower fan assembly enters the combustion chamber through an airway in the mounting flange. Flame is established around the outer wall of the combustion chamber and the fan circulates the products of combustion, quickly establishing a blue flame condition.

The flame detector quickly senses the presence of flame and causes the igniter to be switched off. When the boiler thermostat senses the preset water temperature, the burner motor is switched off and a minimum delay of 96 s must elapse before the thermostat can again initiate the starting cycle.

Natural Draught Pot Vaporising Burner (Fig. 4.3). This is the simplest type of burner and is commonly fitted in heaters with an output in the range 6–18 kW. They are designed to serve central heating boilers or air heaters. The heaters must be connected to a flue capable of creating a draught of 10–20 Pa, depending on the type of heater and its heat output. The burner is almost silent in operation and may be installed in a kitchen or livingroom.

The heat output from the burner may be sufficient to cause high water temperatures and a 'heat leak' in the form of a bathroom radiator or towel rail is frequently recommended.

The burner consists basically of a circular container or pot, which in some cases has a smaller-diameter opening at the top with rows of holes widely separated at the bottom, and close together at the top, to admit the required volume of air for combustion. The holes at the top are sometimes formed so as to cause a swirl to the incoming air, which assists the mixing of the oil vapour and air.

Air is admitted progressively through the holes at the side of the cylinder, so that as the firing rate is increased the flame has to rise up the pot to obtain sufficient air for combustion. Oil is metered at a low flow rate from a constant level controller and spreads a thin film of oil at the base of the pot.

Heat generated by this burning thin film of oil causes vaporisation, and oil vapour rises up the pot but is too thick to ignite and requires more oxygen. When this oil vapour comes into contact with the air entering through the lowest row of holes, it mixes with it and ignites. The flame then increases in size, radiates more heat and the vaporisation

Fig. 4.3 Natural draught oil burner.

process continues. Oil vapour continues to rise and when it obtains sufficient air it ignites until the amount of air mixing with the vapour results in the flame burning out at the top of the pot, as shown in Fig. 4.4.

Note: all appliances equipped with natural draught burners require a draught stabiliser to ensure that a steady draught is maintained at the burner.

The gradual introduction of air is very important, as too much air at the base of the pot would cause the flame to be too close to the oil film, overheating it and causing the formation of carbon deposits.

The high-firing ring at the top of the pot is an important part of the design and forms a throat which promotes the final mixing of air and oil vapour. The burner also contains a low-fire ring above the first row of air holes, but this will not normally allow a low flame below one-third of the high firing rate.

As mentioned previously, overheating of the hot water supply may occur when the central heating is switched off and some form of 'heat leak' is therefore sometimes required.

Fig. 4.4 Natural draught vaporising burner operating on high flame firing.

Forced Draught Pot Burner (Fig. 4.5). The design of this burner is similar to that of the natural draught pot burner, except that the pot is enclosed inside a casing into which air required for combustion is supplied by a fan.

Fig. 4.5 Forced draught draught vaporising burner.

Oil Metering and Constant Level Control. Because the oil feed to vaporising burners requires to maintain a constant level of oil, some form of control is required. The function of the control is to maintain a constant level of oil at the burner, irrespective of the level of oil in the storage tank, and to meter the oil supply to the burner at the correct rate.

Fig. 4.6 shows a section of a double-float constant-head controller which also has a safety function in providing a secondary cut-off should the inlet needle valve continue to pass oil when the correct operating level is exceeded. The controller operates as follows.

1. Oil under pressure from the storage tank flows through the filter and inlet needle valve.

2. The oil is maintained at a constant level by means of float A which raises or lowers the inlet valve as required.

3. When the needle valve makes contact with its seating, it shuts off the supply of oil from the storage tank.

4. The inlet valve normally takes up a position such that the inflow of oil to the burner is sufficient for the heat required.

5. If the needle valve fails to close, because of a faulty seating or dirt accumulating between the valve and

the seating, the oil level rises and flows over the wier into the trip chamber.

6. Float B then rises and actuates the trip mechanism and the spring forces down lever C onto the needle valve. The needle valve is thus forced down against its seating with sufficient force to dislodge any particles of dirt.

Atomising Oil Burners (Fig. 4.7)

Atomisation is an alternative to vaporising the oil before mixing it with air to cause it to burn. Although there are many types of atomising burner, the pressure-jet type is the most common. This is chiefly because of its compact design and relatively silent operation. They are available with outputs of from 15 kW upwards.

The burner operates as follows.

1. Oil is pumped to the atomiser, which breaks up the oil (atomisation) into a very fine spray.

2. The fan forces a controlled amount of air through the air director, so that it mixes with the oil spray. The air director maintains a consistent air pattern, stabilises the flame and creates the required flame shape.

Fig. 4.6   Double-float constant-level oil controller.

Oil-pressure regulating valve

Nozzle shut-off valve

Oil pump

Filter

Oil pipes

Ignition electrodes

Atomiser

Air director

Combustion air inlet ports

Low-pressure centrifugal fan

Electric motor

Control box

Ignition transformer

Fig. 4.7   Automatic pressure jet burner.

3. The oil mixture is ignited by the ignition electrodes, which require 10 kV across the electrodes. The burner then operates in an on/off sequence in accordance with the demands for heat.

Controls

The overall control is electrical and provided by a control panel to which the ignition, thermostat control and safety devices are connected. A boiler thermostat is preset for the boiler water temperature required and determines when the burner is started or stopped. A flame-failure device, in the form of photoelectric cell, senses when the flame fails whilst the burner is running and causes the burner to shut down.

Oil Storage

Generally, a rectangular tank with a top designed to shed water and with a working capacity of 1136 l is satisfactory for installations of up to about 13 kW. It is, however, in the client's interest to install a larger tank so that advantage may be taken of the lower cost of oil delivery in capacities of 2275 l and over.

The largest capacity tank for domestic work is usually 3400 l. The tank should be made from ungalvanised welded carbon steel or sectional pressed ungalvanised steel. The surfaces of the tank should be thoroughly prepared and protected with a rust-inhibiting steel primer and finished with a minimum of two coats of good-quality oil-resistant paint. Fig. 4.8 shows the installation of a domestic oil-storage tank, which requires the following fittings.

1. A 50 mm bore pipe, extended to the edge of the tank, in such a position that the delivery hose can be easily connected. If required, the fill pipe may be extended either above or below ground, to a convenient point of not more than 30 m from the delivery tanker. A buried extension line should

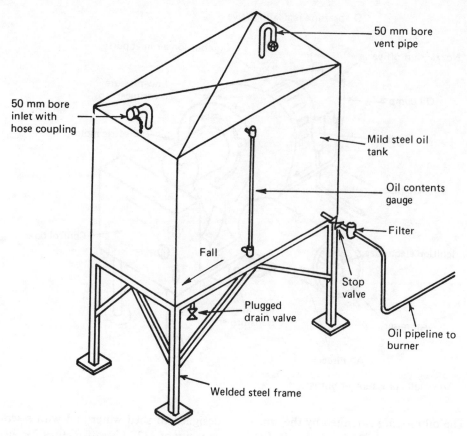

Fig. 4.8 Installation of domestic oil storage tank.

be terminated within a manhole, or the inlet connection must be raised to about 300 mm above ground.

2. A vent pipe must always be fitted and its bore must always be at least equal to that of the fill pipe. It should rise above the tank no more than 600 mm, unless the tank is installed inside a tank room. The open end of the pipe must be fitted with an open-mesh wire balloon. Overflow warning devices must never be fitted to the vent pipe, since with certain types internal tank pressures can rise when the tank is being filled and damage can result.

3. An isolating valve must always be fitted in the tank outlet, in an accessible position for connecting the oil supply. It is important that the tank outlet tapping is slightly above the bottom of the tank to ensure that no

water or sediment can be drawn into the burner. Other fittings include a contents gauge and a plugged drain valve.

Location of Oil Tank

The tank should, if possible, be sited above ground and, for domestic work, in the open. Larger tanks are usually sited inside an oil tank room adjacent to the boiler. Fig. 4.9 shows an oil tank and boiler layout. The wall and self-closing steel door between the tank room and boiler room must have a minimum fire resistance of 4 h for tanks over 4000 l, 2 h for tanks up to 3400 l and 1 h for tanks up to 1250 l.

A tank inside a garage must be separated from the vehicle space by a fire-resisting wall and ventilated to the open air. A tank in the

52

Fig. 4.9   Oil tank and boiler layout.

open and without a fire barrier must be sited at least 1.8 m from the building. The tank should be within 30 m of the oil tanker vehicle access point, unless an extended fill line is provided. The vehicle must not go over the customer's property.

Oil Supply Systems

Annealed copper pipe is excellent for oil supply lines and enables the line to be run with the minimum of joints. Fig. 4.10 a shows the supply to a vaporising burner. These normally require a one-pipe feed system and depend for their supply on an adequate head of oil in the tank. Fig. 4.10 b shows the supply to an atomising burner with a one-pipe feed. The head of oil from the outlet pipe to the centre of the burner must be at least 300 mm. This amount of head will ensure that the oil pump on the burner is always primed. The maximum head above the burner is 3 m. Fig. 4.10 c shows the supply to an atomising burner with a two-pipe feed. This is required when the head of

oil above the burner is insufficient and ensure that the oil pump on the burner is always primed with oil.

Rooftop Boiler Room (Fig. 4.11)

A rooftop boiler room reduces the length of flue pipe to a minimum, saves space and ensures adequate air for combustion. The oil requires to be pumped up to a service tank sited above the boiler burner. The pump is switched on automatically by an oil-level swith fitted to the service tank. An overflow pipe is required on the service tank to prevent overfilling.

Fire Valves

A fire valve is required to shut off the supply of oil to the burner automatically in the case of a fire. There are two main types.
   1.   A mechanical type, comprising a spring-loaded or free-fall weight-operated gate valve held open by a ten-

(a) Supply to vaporising burner

(b) Supply to atomising burner

(c) Two-pipe system

Fig. 4.10 Oil supply to burners.

Fire valve

Rooftop boiler room

Service tank

Oil-proof tanking

Filter

Oil feed pipe

Overflow pipe

Vent

Filling point

Ground level

Oil level gauge

Main oil storage tank

Non-return valves

Filter

Duplicated pumps

Fire valve

Drain valve

Fig. 4.11   Oil supply to rooftop boiler room with oil pipes inside a fire-protected enclosure.

sion wire incorporating a fusible link (see Fig. 4.12). The fusible link is usually sited above the boiler burner and in the event of a fire the link breaks, the tension wire released, and the valve closes under the action of the spring or weight. This type of fire valve is usually suitable for use only in separate boiler houses, since the tension wire cannot usually be installed in a house.

2. A pressure-operated type, comprising a bellows-type valve connected by a capillary tube to a heat-sensitive bulb or phial, which is positioned where it will detect excessive temperature. In the event of a fire, the bulb is overheated, causing an increase in vapour pressure in the system, which expands the bellows inside the valve causing it to close (see Fig. 4.13). This type of fire valve is usually used for domestic oil-fired installations.

Combustion Efficiency Testing

The efficiency of combustion can be assessed by taking measurements of

(a) carbon dioxide (CO_2) content of the flue gases,
(b) temperature of the flue gases,
(c) solids in the flue gases,
(d) flue draught.

Although combustion efficiency testing is applied here to oil-fired installations, the same instruments and methods can also be applied to gas installations. A table for the combustion efficiency for gas, however, would have to be used and this would be supplied by the manufacturer of the testing equipment.

Carbon Dioxide Indicator (Fig. 4.14). This consists of a glass flask containing a liquid reagent and a hand-operated syringe-type pump. To measure the CO_2 content of the flue gases, the plunger valve is first depressed with the indicator upright and the fluid level at zero on the scale. The probe is then inserted into a sampling hole in the flue and the plunger is depressed six times to warm the line and to eliminate air. A sample of the flue gas is then taken by depressing the plunger fully and squeezing the bulb of the pump at least 20 times, ensuring that the plunger remains fully depressed. The connecting plunger is then removed and the indicator inverted twice to

Fig. 4.12 Fusible-link-operated fire valve.

Fig. 4.13 Vapour-pressure-operated fire valve.

Fig. 4.14 Carbon dioxide indicator.

ensure that the sample of gas is fully absorbed by the liquid.

Absorption of CO_2 creates a partial vacuum inside the instrument, so the fluid is forced up the centre of the tube by an amount equal to the CO_2 absorbed. The percentage of CO_2 in the flue gas is then read off the scale against the level of the liquid in the tube. The instrument should continue to be inverted and the readings taken again until a consistent value is obtained.

Temperature of Flue Gases is taken by a thermostat shown in Fig. 4.15.

Solids in flue gases. The instrument used (Fig. 4.16) consists of a metal suction pump and a flexible tube terminating with a probe. A transverse slot in the pump body takes a special filter paper. To take a reading, the pump is first warmed to prevent condensation of the flue gases as they are sampled. A clean filter paper is inserted in the slot and the probe inserted in a test hole in the flue. A sample of flue gas is then drawn through the filter paper with ten full strokes of the pump. The filter paper is then withdrawn and the smoke deposit compared with the smoke scale in Fig. 4.17.

Fig. 4.15   Flue gas thermometer.

Fig. 4.16   Smoke tester.

Fig. 4.17   Smoke scale.

Flue Draught. The instrument used is similar in appearance to the flue gas thermometer except that the probe is a hollow tube and the dial reads Pa instead of °C. The draught has an important bearing on burner efficiency and its value in Pa should equal that specified by the manufacturer of the appliance. Note: the appliance should be run for about 15 min before testing.

Combustion Performance

The values of CO_2 content and stack temperature can now be used by means of Table 4.1 to find the percentage combustion efficiency. From the table, the stack loss percentage figure must be deducted from 100 to give the combustion efficiency.

Table 4.1   Combustion Efficiency

% CO_2	Stack loss (%) at					
	93°C	144°C	204°C	260°C	316°C	371°C
14	9.9	12.1	14.3	16.7	18.7	21.0
13	10.1	12.4	14.8	17.4	19.6	22.0
12	10.3	12.8	15.3	18.0	20.3	22.9
11	10.5	13.2	16.0	18.9	21.4	24.2
10	10.8	13.8	16.8	19.9	22.6	25.6
9	11.3	14.4	17.7	21.1	24.1	27.4
8	11.7	15.3	18.9	22.6	26.0	29.6
7	12.3	16.3	20.4	24.6	29.4	32.6
6	13.2	17.7	22.4	27.2	31.6	36.5
5	14.3	19.8	25.3	31.0	36.2	42.0
4	16.1	22.8	29.6	36.5	43.0	50.0

Example 4.1. During a test on an oil-fired boiler, the CO_2 and flue gas temperature reading were 10% and 260 °C respectively. Find the percentage combustion efficiency.

From Table 4.1, the stack loss for a 10% CO_2 reading and a 260 °C temperature reading gives a stack loss percentage of 19.9; therefore the combustion efficiency will be $19.9 - 100 = 80.1\%$. Satisfactory combustion should take place providing that the smoke number is three or less when burning a domestic fuel oil having a relative density of 0.7 and five or less when burning a domestic fuel oil having a relative density of 0.8.

There are two grades of oil for domestic burners:

1. Class C2 or kerosene,
2. Class D or gas oil (similar to fuel used in diesel engines).

Regular maintenance checks of oil-fired

Table 4.2   Equipment Service Maintenance Schedule

The boiler-burner unit

Vaporising	*Atomising*
1. Inspect the chimney flue-ways, advise the customer if they require sweeping	1. Inspect the chimney flue-ways, advise the customer if they require sweeping
2. Clean the boiler flue-ways	2. Clean the boiler flue-ways
3. Clean burner or pot and renew wicks where necessary	3. Check the combustion chamber refractories and make good where necessary
4. Clean and check electrical ignition and associated controls if necessary	4. Remove nozzle assembly, clean nozzle and electrodes, replace and reset
5. Clean oil feed pipes to burner and check flexible connections	5. Inspect filters, clean or replace where necessary
6. Check filter and check operation of controls	6. Check controls for correct operation
7. If fan fitted, check motor operation: clean impeller blades and air inlet guard where necessary	7. Check for oil leaks
8. Check for oil leaks	8. Check fire valve for correct operation
9. Check fire valve for correct operation	9. Lubricate motor if necessary
10. Set up burner and check combustion efficiency	10. Set up burner and check combustion efficiency
11. Leave the installation in a clean condition	11. Leave the installation in a clean condition

Oil storage
1. Check tank for sludge and drain off where necessary
2. Check tank gauge for correct indication

Heating system
1. Check pump for correct operation
2. Check thermostats for correct operation
3. On warm-air systems, check operation of air distribution fan and air filters

appliances should be made on all mechanical and electrical equipment in accordance with the manufacturers instructions. During the two routine maintenance visits, service will be carried out as shown in Table 4.2.

Chimneys for Oil-Fired Boilers

If the products of combustion of the oil inside the chimney are allowed to cool to the region of the acid dew point temperature, some of the acid will remain inside the chimney and may attack the material from which it is constructed.

Unburnt particles of carbon are also present in the products of combustion and may collect on any rough surfaces or points of change of velocity. When the boiler is fired, the sudden flow of the products of combustion may cause these carbon deposits to be discharged to the atmosphere. To prevent the occurrence of these problems, the following points must be observed.

1. The chimney should be well insulated and lined with acid-resisting material.
2. Bends should be avoided, and if they have to be included they should have a large radius.
3. The draught stabiliser should not permit excessive cool air to enter the chimney.
4. Where two or more boilers are installed, each boiler should have its own chimney or, if a common chimney is unavoidable, the flues connecting the boilers to the chimney must be provided with dampers, so that an idle flue may be closed from the others.

Note: a balanced flue may also be used for oil-fired boilers.

Draught Stabilisers (Fig. 4.18)

A well designed and constructed chimney will often produce excessive draught and to maintain the correct draught for optimum conditions of firing a draught stabiliser is usually fitted at the base of the chimney.

The stabiliser consists of a hinged metal frame having a hinged flap. The hinged flap is set to maintain the required draught conditions and will automatically open to permit cool air to enter the chimney when the draught is too high. The hinged frame acts as an explosion door to relieve excessive pressure inside the chimney; should this occur, the hinged frame is forced open, carrying with it the hinged flap. After this has occurred, the hinged frame and flap automatically close.

Calorific Values of Fuels

The calorific value of a fuel may be defined as the heat energy produced per unit mass or per unit volume of the fuel when it is fully burned. In practice it is necessary to allow for heat losses when using calorific values.

Table 4.3 gives the approximate calorific values of some common fuels. If other factors are known, calorific values may be used to calculate the amount of fuel used for a heating system and the cost.

Example 4.2. Calculate the mass of fuel required per week for a house having heat losses of 20 kW. An oil-fired boiler having an efficiency of 80% and is to be fired for 10 h each day. Calorific value of oil = 45 MJ/kg.

$$kW = \frac{kJ}{s}$$
$$kJ = kW \times s$$
$$kJ = 20 \times 7 \times 10 \times 60 \times 60$$
$$kJ = \frac{20 \times 7 \times 10 \times 60 \times 60 \times 100}{80}$$

Table 4.3 Calorific Values of Fuels

Fuel	Calorific value (MJ/kg)
Coal	30
Wood	18.5
Anthracite	32
Coke	25
Fuel oil (domestic)	45
Natural gas	36 MJ/m³
Electricity	3.6 MJ/kW

Hinged flap

Hinged frame

Frame built into chimney

(a) View of draught stabiliser

Joint made with mineral wool

135° bend

Lined chimney

Boiler

Draught stabiliser

(b) Installation of draught stabiliser

Fig. 4.18 Draught stabiliser.

$$= 6\ 300\ 000$$
$$\text{MJ} = 6300$$
$$\text{mass} = \frac{\text{MJ}}{\text{calorific value (MJ/kg)}}$$
$$= \frac{6300}{45}$$
$$= 140\ \text{kg}$$

Note: once the mass of fuel required is found, the cost may be easily found by multiplying the cost per kg by the mass required in kg. The cost of fuel increases rapidly, but assuming that the cost of 1 kg of oil is 5p, the running cost per week for the house heating system would be

$$= 5 \times 140$$
$$= 700\text{p}$$
$$= £7.00$$

Exercises

1. Explain why it is essential to vaporise or atomise oil before it can be burned.
2. Sketch and explain the operation of the following types of oil burner;
   (a) wallflame,
   (b) dynaflame.
3. Sketch and explain the operation of natural and forced-draught vaporising burners and state why it is necessary to provide a heat leak with these types of burner.
4. State the purpose of a constant level controller. Sketch a section through a double-float constant-level controller and explain its operation.
5. Sketch an elevation of a pressure-jet atomising burner and explain its operation.
6. State the usual capacities of oil tanks for small installations and the type of material required for their construction.
7. Sketch an isometric view of an oil-storage tank showing all the necessary controls and pipework.
8. State the usual positions for the siting of an oil storage tank.
9. Sketch the method of supplying oil to a rooftop boiler room.
10. Sketch a section through an oil tank room showing the method of installing the oil tank and the necessary fire precautions.
11. State the purpose of a fire valve. Sketch and explain the operation of the following types of fire valve:
    (a) mechanical,
    (b) liquid expansion.
12. Sketch and describe the method of carrying out a combustion efficiency test on an oil-fired boiler.
13. Sketch a chimney for an oil-fired boiler and state the types of material that may be used for its construction.
14. Sketch and explain the operation of a draught stabiliser.
15. Define the term 'calorific value of fuel' and state the calorific values of coal, anthracite, fuel oil, natural gas and electricity.

Chapter 5
Centralised Hot Water Supply, Pipe Sizing

Definitions

BOILER HEATING SURFACES:

(a) DIRECT: in which the surfaces of the boiler receive heat directly from the heat source,

(b) INDIRECT: in which the surfaces of the boiler receive heat indirectly from the fire, usually through internal flue ways.

BOILER-RATED OUTPUT: the power of the boiler rated in kilowatts.

CALORIFIER: a vessel in which water is heated by means of an internal heat exchanger.

COLD FEED PIPE: a pipe connecting the cistern to the hot water system.

COMBINED BOILER AND STORAGE VESSEL: a boiler unit on which is super-imposed a storage vessel.

DEAD LEG: a single pipe for drawing off hot water from a calorifier, cylinder or tank.

FEED AND EXPANSION CISTERN: an open-top vessel for maintaining the water level in the system and for accommodating increases in the volume of water due to expansion.

HEAD TANK: an auxiliary hot water storage vessel with open vent, used to ensure an adequate supply of hot water to certain draw-off points.

HOT WATER CYLINDER: a closed cylindrical vessel in which hot water is stored.

HOT WATER TANK: a closed rectangular vessel in which hot water is stored.

INDIRECT CYLINDER: a term usually used to define a small domestic storage calorifier.

ISOLATING VALVE: a valve used to isolate a circuit.

NOMINAL CAPACITY: the total volume of a cistern, tank or cylinder, calculated from the external dimensions of these vessels.

OPEN VENT: an open pipe from any high point in a hot-water system or from any closed vessel containing hot water.

PRIMARY CIRCUIT: the flow and return pipes through which hot water circulates between the boiler (or other heating appliance) and the storage vessel.

SECONDARY CIRCUIT: the flow and return pipes through which hot water circulates between the storage vessel and the hot-water draw off points.

Centralised Systems

In a centralised system, water is heated and stored centrally and distributed throughout the building by means of pipework. The heating of the water is usually achieved by means of a boiler which may be fired by gas, oil or solid fuel. The hot water is stored inside a cylinder or calorifier and these should be sited as close as possible to the boiler, so that the heat losses from the primary circuit is reduced to a minimum. A combined boiler and storage vessel would reduce these heat losses to the absolute minimum.

The hot water storage vessel should be well lagged and, in large systems for hospitals, schools, factories, etc., the primary and secondary circuits should be lagged.

A centralised system has the following advantages.

1. The hot water storage vessel contains sufficient water to meet a large anticipated peak demand load. This is important for large buildings where bulk supplies are required.
2. It may be possible to use cheaper fuel, i.e. lower-grade oil or solid fuel.
3. The risk of a fire inside the building is greatly reduced and confined to the boiler room.
4. One boiler plant reduces maintenance.

There are two distinct types of system: direct and indirect.

Direct Systems. In these, the water in the boiler circulates direct to the hot water storage vessel without passing through a heat exchanger. The system is cheap to install and the direct circulation provides a quick heat-recovery period. If soft water is used, the boiler must be rustproofed or rusty water will be drawn off through the taps. In temporary hard water districts there is a risk of scaling of the boiler and primary circuit, and the water temperature must therefore never exceed 60 °C, otherwise excessive scaling will occur.

Indirect Systems. In these, the water in the boiler circulates through a heat exchanger fitted inside the hot water storage vessel and the water is heated indirectly. If steam is available this may be circulated through the heat exchanger instead of hot water.

Since the water in the boiler does not mix with the water in the storage vessel, in soft water districts there is no risk of rusty water being drawn off through the taps. Because the water in the boiler, primary circuit and heat exchanger is not drawn off through the taps, there is no risk of scaling when temporary hard water is used.

After initial heating of the water and precipitation of the carbonates, there should

be no further occurrences of this precipitation. Indirect systems have a further advantage when central heating is combined with the hot water supply, because there is no risk of rusty water from the radiators being drawn off through the taps. The water temperature may also be higher than that used for the direct system, which is necessary for the central heating system.

Domestic Installations. In domestic buildings the water is heated by a floor or wall-mounted boiler, or by a back boiler behind the living room grate. Fig. 5.1 shows a direct system to supply bath, basin, sink, shower and towel airer, and Fig. 5.2 shows an indirect system for supplying the same fittings.

Primatic Cylinder (Fig. 5.3)

A saving in the cost of an indirect system can be achieved by the use of a single-feed cylinder. The cylinder is provided with a patented heat exchanger, which is designed to provide two airlocks between the primary and secondary waters. These airlocks prevent mixing of the two waters and the cylinder thus acts in the same way as a conventional indirect cylinder with a heating coil. The cylinder dispenses with an expansion and feed cistern, primary feed pipe and primary vent pipe. Fig. 5.4 shows the installation of the primatic cylinder: although it is an indirect system, the system is installed similar to the direct system.

Sealed Primary Circuits

If a conventional indirect cylinder is required, an alternative method of dispensing with the expansion and feed cistern involves the use of a sealed primary circuit. To provide an expansion space for the heated water, an expansion vessel must be fitted to the circuit, usually on the return pipe where the water temperature is lower. Fig. 5.5 shows a cistern-fed indirect system, which is usually permitted in the UK.

Cold-water storage cistern

19 mm bore (minimum) vent pipe

Note: the 450 mm horizontal pipe is to prevent heat loss by one-pipe circulation

Hot water

Cooler water

One-pipe circulation

Gate valve

450 mm (minimum)

Basin

Bath

25 mm bore cold feed pipe

136 l capacity (minimum) insulated cylinder

19 mm bore (minimum)

13 mm bore (minimum)

Basin

25 mm or 32 mm bore primary flow and return pipes

Drain valve

Sink

Boiler

Safety valve

Drain valve

Fig. 5.1   Direct hot-water supply system.

The Building Regulations 1992 permit the use of unvented hot water storage systems. The secondary circuit is fed directly from the water main, which dispenses with the cold water storage cistern, secondary cold feed and vent pipe.

Because the hot water storage vessel is subjected to pressure from the water main, the metal will have to be thicker than for a cistern-fed storage vessel. As an alternative to the use of thicker metal, a pressure-reducing valve may be installed on the cold water ser-

Cold-water storage cistern

Gate valve

Expansion and feed cistern

19 mm bore (minimum) secondary vent pipe

19 mm bore (minimum) primary vent pipe

13 mm bore (minimum) primary cold feed pipe

Bath

Basin

Drain valve

136 l capacity (minimum) insulated indirect cylinder

25 mm or 32 mm bore primary flow and return pipes

Sink

Boiler

Basin

Drain valve

Safety valve

Drain valve

Fig. 5.2   Indirect hot-water supply system.

Fig. 5.3 Primatic cylinder.

Electric immersion heater boss

Hot-water supply pipe and vent

Cold feed pipe

Level of primary water

Air

Air

Primary flow pipe

Drain valve

Primary return pipe

Bath

Basin

Primatic cylinder

Drain valve

Fig. 5.4 Installation of primatic cylinder.

Sink

Boiler

Drain valve

Fig. 5.5   Cistern-fed system with sealed primary circuit.

vice pipe supplying the vessel.

Fig. 5.6 shows a mains-fed unvented hot water storage system with a sealed primary circuit. The hot water storage cylinder should be an approved well-lagged proprietary unit or package. The system must be installed by qualified plumbers or heating engineers.

Systems for Large Buildings

Because the local water authorities prevent

the use of long 'dead legs', it is necessary in a large building to provide a secondary return back to the hot water calorifier. A dead leg can result in a great deal of water being wasted because each time water is drawn off through the taps cooler water in the pipe must first be run to waste. Table 5.1 gives the maximum lengths of hot water draw-off pipes not requiring insulation.

Since hot water is allowed to circulate when a secondary return is installed, the hot water

Fig. 5.6 Mains-fed unvented hot water storage system

Note: the non-return valve and anti-vacuum valve prevent siphonage of water (in the cylinder and draw-off taps) back into the water main

will follow immediately through the draw-off taps, thus preventing waste of water. This immediate supply of hot water is also more convenient to the occupants of the building. Fig. 5.7 shows an indirect system for a three-storey building and, if required, the secondary circuit may be pumped. Fig. 5.8

Table 5.1 Building Regulations for the maximum lengths of hot water draw-off pipes not requiring insulation

Outside diameter of pipe (mm)	Maximum length of uninsulated pipe (m)
Not more than 12	20
More than 12 but not more than 22	12
More than 22 but not more than 28	8
More than 28	3

shows other types of secondary circuit that may be used for the building.

Steam-Heated Calorifier

In hospitals and factories where the space heating is by the use of steam, it is very convenient to install a steam-heated storage calorifier to provide hot water for supplying the ablution fittings. Fig. 5.9 shows the installation of a horizontal steam-heated storage calorifier.

Supplies to High-Rise Buildings (Fig. 5.10)

To prevent excessive water pressures on the lowest draw-off points, and consequent risk of water hammer and wear on valves, it is essential that the head of water acting on these points does not exceed 30 m. In build-

Cold-water storage cistern

Isolating valves

Drain valve

Draw-off points

Secondary flow pipe

Secondary return pipe

Pump

Calorifier

Air valve

Sealed primary circuit

Expansion vessel

Nitrogen

Boiler

Fig. 5.7 Hot-water supply system for a three-storey building.

Fig. 5.8 Secondary circuits.

Fig. 5.9 Steam-heated storage calorifier.

ings above 30 m in height, therefore, two or more secondary circuits will be required. Each circuit must be supplied with water from a separate cold water storage cistern. The primary circuit may be sealed as shown, or fed from an open expansion and feed cistern.

Stand-By Plant (Fig. 5.11)

In buildings where it is essential to maintain a supply of hot water at all times, a stand-by plant will have to be installed.

The insertion of isolating valves as shown will allow either a boiler or a calorifier to be repaired or replaced whilst still maintaining a supply of hot water from the remaining plant. The three-way vent valve will ensure that the primary circuit is open to the atmosphere at all times, even when the stop valves are closed.

Solar Heating of Water (Fig. 5.12)

The heating of water by use of a flat-plate solar collector sited on the roof may save up to 40% of the heating cost of hot water

supply. For a house, the collector should have an area of between 4 m² and 6 m² and be fixed at an angle of about 40 ° facing south.

Solar Collector. This consists of an aluminium alloy or copper frame with a sealed glass cover. A copper radiator or copper pipes, painted black, are fixed inside the frame so that there is an air space of about 20 mm between the glass and the radiator or pipes.

Aluminium foil should be fixed behind the radiator or pipes and 75–100 mm thickness of insulation fixed behind the foil. Fig. 5.13 shows a section through a solar collector.

Operation of the System.

1. The flat-plate collector is heated by solar radiation, which in turn heats a mixture of water and antifreeze inside the radiator or pipes to a temperature of up to 60 °C. On a sunny day it is possible to heat by solar energy all the water required for a house.

2. The pump is switched on when the temperature of thermostat A exceeds the temperature of thermostat B by between 2 and 3 °C.

3. The water and antifreeze in the solar collector is pumped through the heat

Fig. 5.10 High-rise building.

Fig. 5.11 Stand-by plant. s.r. = secondary return, n.r.v. = non-return valve, s.f. = secondary flow, s.v. = secondary vent, p.v. = primary vent, a.v. = air valve, p.f. = primary flow, s.c.f. = secondary cold feed, d.v. = drain valve, 3w.v.v. = three-way vent valve, p.r. = primary return, r.v. = relief valve, p.c.f. = primary cold feed.

Fig. 5.13 Flat-plate solar collector.

Fig. 5.12 Solar hot-water system.

The following labels appear in the figure:

- Thermostat A
- Air valve
- Solar collector
- Solar system filled with nontoxic antifreeze
- Pressure gauge
- Pressure relief valve
- Control panel
- Non-return valve
- Pump
- Filling point
- Expansion vessel
- Thermostat B
- Vent pipes
- Cold-water storage cistern
- Well insulated 200 l solar cylinder
- Well insulated 136-l coventional cylinder
- To hot-water taps
- Flow and return pipes to boiler

exchanger inside the 200 l solar cylinder and the heat exchanger heats the water.

4. When hot water is drawn off through the hot water taps, the cold water from the cold water storage cistern forces hot water from the solar cylinder into the conventional cylinder and this reduces or eliminates the heat required to raise the temperature of the water in the conventional cylinder.

Note: to prevent loss of fluid in the solar circuit, a sealed system is used. The expansion vessel contains a rubber diaphragm with one side in contact with the fluid and the other side in contact with a cushion of nitrogen gas.

Hot Water Storage Requirement and Boiler Power

If the population of the building is known these may be calculated by use of Table 5.2.

Example 5.1. Calculate the hot water storage requirements and the boiler power for a factory having 250 employees, using Table 5.2.

$$\begin{aligned} \text{Storage} \\ \text{requirement} &= 250 \times 5 \\ &= 1250 \text{ l} \\ \text{Boiler power} &= 250 \times 1.2 \\ &= 300 \text{ kW} \end{aligned}$$

Combined Hot and Cold Water Unit (Fig. 5.14)

A factory-made self-contained unit for providing hot and cold water for sink, bath, basin and WC will save a great deal of work on site. The unit is based on a design developed by the Research and Development Group of the Ministry of Housing and Local Government, and is acceptable for the appropriate government improvement grant. It is readily handled upstairs and through doorways and may be in a cupboard, in a passage or convenient corner, or incorporated in the structure of new housing.

Table 5.2 Hot Water Storage and Boiler Power

Note: the temperature of the cold feed water to the hot water storage is assumed to be 10 °C. For other temperatures the boiler power will have to be increased or reduced as appropriate.

	Storage power at 65 °C (l/person)	Boiler to 65 °C (kW/person)
Colleges and schools		
boarding	25	0.7
day	5	0.1
Dwellings and flats		
low rental	25	0.5
medium rental	30	0.7
high rental	45	1.2
Factories	5	1.2
Hospitals		
general	30	1.5
infectious	45	1.5
infirmaries	25	0.6
infirmaries with laundry	30	0.9
maternity	30	2.1
mental	25	0.7
Nurses' homes	45	1.2
Hostels	35	0.9
Offices	5	0.1
Sports pavilions	35	0.3

Pipe Sizing for Hot and Cold Water

The internal diameter of a hot or cold water pipe required to discharge a given amount of water when subjected to a certain head or pressure of water may be found from tables or charts or by calculation.

A well known formula for the sizing of hot and cold water pipes was devised by Thomas Box and is expressed as follows:

$$q = \sqrt{\left(\frac{d^5 \times H}{25 \times L \times 10^5} \right)}$$

where q is the discharge through the pipe in l/s, d is the diameter of the pipes in mm, H is the head of water in m, and L is the effective length of pipe in m.

76

Fig. 5.14 Combined hot and cold water unit.

Example 5.2. Calculate the diameter of a pipe to discharge 0.2 l/s to a shower when there is a constant head of water of 1.5 m and an effective length of pipe of 5 m. Note: to find the diameter of the pipe, the Box's formula will have to be transposed to give an expression for diameter and this will be shown to help students unfamiliar with transposition. Most students possess a pocket calculator, but the ability to use logarithms is still required and logarithms have therefore been used in the calculation.

$$q = \sqrt{\frac{d^5 \times H}{25 \times L \times 10^5}}$$

Squaring both sides,

$$q^2 = \frac{d^5 \times H}{25 \times L \times 10^5}$$

and cross-multiplying,

$$q^2 \times 25 \times L \times 10^5 = d^5 \times H$$

Dividing both sides by H,

$$d^5 = \frac{q^2 \times 25 \times L \times 10^5}{H}$$

and taking the fifth root of both sides,

$$d = \sqrt[5]{\frac{q^2 \times 25 \times L \times 10^5}{H}}$$

Therefore

$$d = \sqrt[5]{\frac{0.2^2 \times 25 \times 5 \times 10^5}{1.5}}$$

By logs:

Number	Log
0.04	$\bar{2}.6021$
25	1.3979
5	0.6990
10^5	5.0000
	5.6990
1.5	0.1761
(5th root) ($\div 5$)	5.5129
12.6	1.1025

A 13 mm bore pipe would be satisfactory.

Relative Discharging Power of Pipes

The relative discharging powers of pipes are as the square root of the fifth power of their diameters.

$$N = \sqrt{\left(\frac{D}{d}\right)^5}$$

where N is the number of branch pipes, D is the diameter of main pipe, and d is the diameter of branch pipes.

Example 5.3. Calculate the diameter of a water pipe to supply five washbasins each having a 13 mm diameter short branch pipe.

$$N = \sqrt{\left(\frac{D}{d}\right)^5}$$

squaring both sides,

$$N^2 = \left(\frac{D}{d}\right)^5$$

Taking the fifth root of both sides,

$$\sqrt[5]{N^2} = \frac{D}{d}$$

Multiplying both sides by d,

$$D = \sqrt[5]{N^2} \times d$$

Therefore

$$D = \sqrt[5]{5^2} \times 13$$

By logs,

Number	Log
25	1.3979
(5th root) ($\div 5$)	1.3979
	0.2795
13	1.1139
24.74	1.3934

A 25 mm bore main pipe would be satisfactory.

Exercises

1. Define the following terms:
   (a) boiler heating surfaces,
   (b) boiler power,
   (c) calorifier,
   (d) dead leg,
   (e) feed and expansion cistern,
   (f) secondary circuit,
   (g) head tank.
2. State the principles of design of a centralised system of hot water supply.
3. Describe the direct and indirect systems of hot water supply and state the advantages of an indirect system over a direct system.
4. Sketch isometric diagrams of both direct and indirect systems of hot water supply for a house having bath, shower, basin, sink and towel rail.
5. State the advantages of a single-feed hot water cylinder and sketch a section through the cylinder and explain its operation.
6. Sketch a 'sealed' primary circuit and state its advantages over an 'open' primary circuit.
7. Sketch and annotate an isometric diagram of an indirect hot water system for a two-storey hotel having two bathrooms on each floor, each containing bath, basin and towel rail. The boiler and calorifier are to be sited on the ground floor adjacent to the bathrooms.
8. State the principles of design of a centralised hot water supply system for a high-rise building and sketch a system suitable for a 15-storey hotel having two

bathrooms on each floor, each containing bath, shower, basin and towel rail.

9. Sketch a section through a horizontal steam-heated storage calorifier showing all necessary valves and fittings.

10. Two boilers and two calorifiers are to be interconnected so that each appliance may be isolated for repair or renewal. Show by means of sketches the method of installing the boilers and calorifiers so that this can be achieved.

11. State the principles of design of a solar-heated hot water supply system. Sketch a solar system suitable for a house and explain its operation.

12. Calculate the hot water storage requirements and the boiler power for an office having 300 employees (Use Table 5.2.)

13. Calculate the diameter of a main pipe to supply thirty 19 mm diameter short branch pipes.

14. Calculate the head of water (in metres) required to discharge 5 l/s through a 50 mm bore pipe having an effective length of 45 m.

15. Calculate the number of 25 mm diameter branch pipes that may be supplied from a 76 mm diameter main pipe.

16. Calculate the diameter of a pipe to discharge 2 l/s when the effective length of pipe is 12 m and the head of water is 4 m.

Chapter 6
Localised Water Heating Systems

Principles

Instead of a centralised plant for the heating and storage of the hot water, localised systems, as the name implies, use electric or gas water heaters sited either directly over the fitting being supplied or as close as possible to the fitting. The lengths of the pipework and the heat losses from them are therefore reduced considerably and the cost of constructing a boiler room is eliminated. The heaters, however, take up a certain amount of wall or floor space within the building.

Electric Heaters

At the present time, the cost of heating water by electricity is higher than heating by other fuels and great care is required when designing a system in order to reduce the heat losses to the minimum. The following points must therefore be observed when installing a system using electric water heaters.

1. The lengths of the hot water supply pipes must be as short as possible, especially to the sink. The sink is normally used more than any other fitting and each time hot water is drawn off, hot water is left inside the pipe, which cools and loses heat.
2. The hot water storage vessel must be well insulated with a minimum of 50 mm thickness and preferably 76 mm of good-quality insulating material.

3. All circulation of electrically heated water must be avoided and therefore towel rails and radiators must not be installed on the system.
4. 'Single pipe' circulation in the hot water supply pipe or vent pipe must be avoided. In a system using a two-in-one pressure-type heater, this is achieved by carrying the hot water supply pipe from the top of the heater at least 450 mm horizontally before it connects to the vertical pipe as shown in Fig. 6.2.
5. The electric element must be controlled by a thermostat so that the water temperature does not exceed 60 °C in hard water areas and 70 °C in soft water areas.
6. Airing cupboards must not be heated by leaving part of the hot water storage vessel uninsulated. There is sufficient heat for airing linen from the exposed hot water pipes inside the airing cupboard.

Open-Outlet Single-Point Heaters (Fig. 6.1). All heaters of this type are designed to serve one fitting at a time. It is possible, however, to install the heater between two adjacent fittings so that the swivel open outlet can be turned to supply both fittings. Capacities vary from 1.5 to 68.1. The heater may be connected direct from the water main or a cold water cistern.

Anti-drip device

Level of hot water

Level of water after draw-off

Immersion heater

Metal casing

Rod thermostat

Insulation

Swivel joint

Baffle

Cold-water inlet

Hot-water outlet pipe

Fig. 6.1 Open-outlet electric water heater.

The baffle on the cold feed pipe prevents undue mixing of the cold water entering with the hot water inside the heater. The 'anti-drop' device prevents a drip of water through the outlet when the water is being heated and expands.

Pressure-Type Heaters (Fig. 6.2). These heaters are designed for use when hot water is required for two or more fittings. All models are totally enclosed and fed from a storage or feed cistern: they must never be supplied with cold water directly from the water main. The heater is normally fitted with two immersion heaters; one near the top, which is switched on for basin and sink use, and a larger heater at the bottom, which is switched on when larger quantities of water are required for bath and laundry use.

Fig. 6.3 shows the installation of a heater for a house. The heater is fitted near the sink to reduce the length of the hot water pipe. Fig. 6.4 shows the installation of a pressure heater for a three-storey building.

To prevent hot water from the heaters on the upper floors flowing down to the heaters below, the branch connections to the cold feed pipe must be taken above the heaters. The cold feed pipe must be vented at the top to prevent siphoning of hot water from the heaters on the upper floors down to the heaters on the lower floors. This could occur

Vent pipe

450 mm (minimum)

Hot-water outlet

Rod thermostat

500 W
element

Fig. 6.2   Two-in-one pressure-type
electric water heater.

Insulation

Rod thermostat

2500 W
element on
foot control

Cold-water inlet

Cold-water storage cistern

Vent pipe

Basin   Bath

Cold-feed pipe

Sink

Fig. 6.3   Two-in-one pressure-type water heater
for a house.

Drain valve

Cold-water storage cistern

Vent pipes

Pressure heater

Cold-feed pipe

Drain valve

Drain valve

Hot-water draw-offs

Fig. 6.4 Two-in-one pressure heaters in a three- storey building.

when the stop valve on the cold water storage cistern is closed.

If required, the heaters on each floor can be supplied from separate cold water storage cisterns. This method is required when the heaters are installed in high-rise buildings to prevent excessive water pressure inside the storage vessels.

Capacities of heaters vary between 55 and 455 l. A 90 l capacity is very popular for domestic work with a 500 W immersion

heater in the top and a 2500 W immersion heater in the bottom. The bottom heater is normally operated by a foot switch.

Cistern-Type Heaters (Fig. 6.5). This type contains an integral cold water feed cistern fixed immediately above the hot water storage vessel, which is insulated. It is therefore a complete water heating installation and only requires connections for the cold water service pipe, hot water supply pipe, overflow

83

Fig. 6.5   Cistern-type electric water heater.

pipe and electrical service. Rectangular and circular models are manufactured for wall fixing, in capacities from 25 to 140 l of hot water storage. The base of the heater should always be higher than the highest hot water draw-off taps served.

Fig. 6.6 shows the installation of the cistern-type heaters for a three-storey building. The cold water supply to the heaters is shown connected to a cold water storage cistern. If the water mains pressure is sufficient, the heaters may be connected directly to the main.

Some units employ a variable-volume constant-temperature principle in which the cold water feed pipe is restricted to allow the

electric immersion heater to heat the inflowing cold water quickly.

Instantaneous Heaters (Fig. 6.7). As the name implies, these heaters heat the cold water instantly as it flows through the heater, and storage of hot water is therefore not required. The heaters are much smaller than the other types of heater and are very popular for shower and washbasin use. The shower has an electric loading of 6 kW and will provide a continuous supply of warm water at showering temperature up to a maximum rate of approximately 3 l/min. The washbasin-type heater has an electrical loading of 3 kW and will provide a continuous supply of warm

84

Fig. 6.6 Cistern heaters in a three-storey building.

Fig. 6.7 Instantaneous electric water heater.

water for hand washing at the rate of approximately 1.4 l/min. The warm water passes through a spray head of a swivel arm and is ample for washing hands, but is not recommended for sinks, where greater amounts of water at higher temperatures are required. A storage type with open outlet previously described would therefore be required.

The heaters incorporate a pressure switch which will not allow the heating element to be switched on until water is flowing and vice versa. A preset thermal cut-out switch is also incorporated as a safeguard against overheating of the water. The heaters are usually connected directly to the water main. Fig. 6.8 shows the installation of a shower heater and

Fig. 6.9 shows the installation of a washbasin heater.

Rod-Type Thermostat (Fig. 6.10)

All heating elements must be thermostatically controlled. The thermostat used for water heating consists of rod of invar steel (nickel steel) which expands very little, fixed inside a tube of brass which has a greater coefficient of expansion. When the brass tube, which is in contact with the water, expands, it pulls out the invar rod with it and breaks the electrical contact. The permanent magnet ensures a snap-action contact.

Fig. 6.8   Instantaneous shower heater.

Fig. 6.9   Instantaneous wash basin heater.

Fig. 6.10   Rod thermostat.

In breaking the circuit, the contacts are moved only a very short distance apart. This distance is often termed a 'micro-gap' and is not sufficient to extinguish the arc that is set up as the circuit is broken. The extinguishing of the arc, however, is done automatically by alternations of the supply when the voltage during the cycle reaches zero. The contacts themselves are relatively large in size and thus cool the arc to such an extent that it is prevented from restriking when the voltage reaches its maximum value again.

Economy 7, Off-Peak Electric Water Heating

The Economy 7, off-peak electric water heating (known as 'Total Heating') is ideal for dwellings which use electrical power for the main water or space heating. The heating takes place for seven hours during the off-peak period, usually between 12 midnight and 7am. The cost of electricity during this period is less than half the standard domestic tariff. The standing charge for Economy 7 is however higher than for the standard domestic tariff but this can be quickly offset by the use of the much cheaper Economy 7 units.

Table 6.1 gives the approximate prices but a check must be made with the regional Electricity Company for prices locally (adding the appropriate VAT).

The Economy 7 Meter To change to Economy 7 water heating a two-rate meter and tariff timeswitch must be fitted. The main function of the tariff timeswitch is to cause the Economy 7 meter to record on the low rate dial for the seven hour off-peak period and then switch to the standard rate tariff dial for the remaining 17 hours.

Hot Water Cylinder The aim of the Economy 7 system is to rely as much as possible on heating the water overnight at the cheap off-peak rate and to limit the use of daytime units. To achieve this, a larger hot water cylinder is preferable, usually 210 litres instead of the standard 144 litres. The cylinder must have a well-fitting insulation jacket 80 mm thick or a factory applied insulation 50−60 mm thick. The insulation will reduce heat loss and ensure that the water remains hot until required.

Immersion heaters It is preferable to have separate immersion heaters for night and day operation. The night element should heat as much water as possible at the cheap rate. The daytime element should be positioned to provide a rapid, economic top-up when required by heating a smaller quantity of water, and should be controlled by a one-hour timer which switches off the element automatically.

Fig. 6.11 shows a Maxistore Cylinder package having a capacity of 210 litres. The package is specially designed for off-peak electric water heating.

Dual top-entry immersion heater (Fig. 6.12) A dual-element immersion heater is

Table 6.1 Approximate Prices of Electricity

Uses	Cost per unit (kWh)	Standing charge per unit (kWh)
Standard domestic tariff, Full 24 hours	8.5p	1.8p
Economy 7, 7 hours at night off-peak	3.5p	0.3p
Economy 7, 17 hours peak-time	8.8p	2.0p

Note: These prices are for guidance only and current prices may be obtained from the local Electricity Company.

Hot water supply pipe

Cable from consumer unit

Rod thermostat with temperature setting of between 50°C and 55°C

Electrical control box

3 kW Maxistore immersion heater with heater 355 mm long and thermostat 280 mm long for top-up use

Cable

Extra-thick factory applied insulation

Rod thermostat with temperature setting of between 60°C and 65°C

Baffle to project cold water downwards and minimise mixing with hot water

Special aluminium rod to protect against corrosion

Cold water feed pipe

3 kW Maxistore immersion heater with heater 355 mm long and 280 mm long thermostat for off-peak operation

Fig. 6.11 Maxistore Cylinder package (210 litre capacity)

available which may be used for converting an existing cylinder with a top entry boss. The long element has a loading concentrated at the lower end of the heater. This arrangement heats water more efficiently by using the long element at night to heat about 105 litres of water to above 40°C. The short element is used during the day if extra hot water is required

and heats only the top 55 litres of water which is enough for a bath.

Thermostats are an integral part of the immersion heaters and are normally set at about 60°C.

Single Top-entry Immersion Heater (Fig. 6.13) Whilst the two side-entry and dual top-

Fig. 6.12   Dual top-entry immersion heater

Fig. 6.13   Single top-entry immersion heater

entry immersion heaters provide the best arrangements the single top-entry immersion heater is the most common. It is used for existing cylinders and the usual capacity is 120 litres. The immersion heater with its thermostat must extend well down in the cylinder to provide the maximum store of hot water.

Unvented Systems

Unvented systems are supplied as a complete unit including all the necessary controls and safety devices. Cold water is supplied direct from the main to the unvented unit via a stopvalve, drain valve, strainer non-return valve, expansion vessel and pressure relief valve.

Gas Water Heaters

There are three main types of gas water heaters; instantaneous, storage and circulator.

Instantaneous Heaters (Fig. 6.14). These provide instant hot water and the water is heated as it passes through a heat exchanger, which is heated by the hot products of combustion. They are obtainable in the following four classes.

1. Bath heaters: these are fitted with a swivel spout outlet to serve both bath and washbasin.
2. Boiling water heaters: these are fitted with a swivel spout outlet and provide boiling water for brewing tea. A humming device fitted to the heater sounds when the water is boiling.
3. Sink heaters: these are fitted with a swivel spout outlet to provide hot water for sink use. These heaters may also be fitted over a washbasin and, if two washbasins are fitted adjacent to each other, the heater may be fitted between to serve both basins.
4. Multipoint heaters: as the name implies, these heaters may serve several fittings, such as a range of washbasins or bath, basin, sink and shower. Fig. 6.15 shows a multipoint heater for a house and Fig. 6.16 shows a multipoint heater connected to an existing hot water supply system. When the solid fuel boiler is out, hot water may be obtained from the heater by closing valve A and opening valve B.

When a hot water tap is opened, cold water passes through a venturi tube, creating a differential pressure across a flexible diaphragm. This moves the diaphragm, which is fixed to a spring-loaded valve, and allows gas to flow to the burner, where the pilot flame ignites it. The cold water flows up to the finned heat exchanger, where it is heated to the required temperature before flowing out to the open hot water tap. When the hot water tap is closed, water ceases to flow and the gas valve is closed by the action of the spring. A bi-metal flame-failure device (Chapter 2) is also fitted, which will shut off the supply of gas to the burner should the pilot flame be extinguished. The multipoint heater will deliver between 5.6 and 6.9 l/min at a temperature of about 65 °C. The head of water above the heater for operation of the valve and correct flow rate should be at least 3 m. The above description gives the basic principles of operation. Modern heaters, however, have an electronic circuit which improves reliability by reducing the number of moving parts. A push button operates a spark ignition to start the boiler.

Storage Heaters (Fig. 6.17). The hot water in these heaters is stored inside a well insulated copper cylinder. There are two types.

1. Storage multipoint heater: these, like the instantaneous multipoint heater, may supply a range of washbasins, or bath, basin and sink, as shown in Fig. 6.18. Common hot water storage capacities of the heaters range from 84 to 114 l. The heater may be connected to a balanced flue.
2. Storage sink heaters: these, like the open-outlet single-point electric water heaters, are designed to serve one fitting at a time and are provided with a swivel spout outlet. They may be supplied with cold water direct from the main (depending upon the local water authority regulations) or from a cold water feed or storage cistern. The hot water storage capacities range from 9 to 23 l.

Note: a combination gas boiler and hot water cylinder for central heating and hot water supply has been recently brought on the market. The unit eliminates the often long primary flow and return pipes and also reduces the cost of installing heating and hot

Draught diverter

Final heat exchanger
with finned copper
pipe

Enamelled
steel casing

Primary heat
exchanger

Pilot flame

Burner

Diaphragm

Hot-water
outlet pipe

Stop valve

Gas cock

Venturi

Cold-water inlet

Gas supply
pipe

Fig. 6.14 Instantaneous gas water heater.

Cold-water storage cistern

Bath

Basin

Cold-feed pipe

Fig. 6.15 Instantaneous multi-point gas water heater for a house.

Basin in cloakroom

Sink

Hot-water supply pipe

Fig. 6.16 Gas storage heater.

Water

Cold-water inlet

Flue

Thermostat

Gas supply

Gas cock

Burner

Thermostatic valve

Fig. 6.17 Instaneous gas water heater connected to existing system.

Fig. 6.18 Installation of gas storage heater.

water supply. The unit comprises a 77 l capacity cylinder and an 11.7 kW boiler, which enables a 20 min hot water recovery to be achieved following a large demand (e.g. a bath).

Circulators (Fig. 6.19). These heaters are connected to the hot water storage cylinder with flow and return pipes. The heater may provide the sole means of providing hot water, or be connected to an existing hot water supply system having a solid fuel boiler and then used as an auxiliary heater (see Fig. 6.20).

When the solid fuel boiler is out, the circulator may be used in the same way as an electric immersion heater, to provide hot water. To conserve fuel, a three-way economy valve should be fitted to the return pipe. When large quantities of hot water are required, the valve can be operated so that the

bottom return pipe is opened and the top return pipe closed; this allows the whole content of water inside the cylinder to be heated. When small quantities of hot water are required for sink and basin use, the valve can be operated so that the bottom return pipe is closed and the top return pipe opened; this allows only a small quantity of water at the top of the cylinder to be heated.

The usual water output of a circulator is about 25 l/h raised through a temperature of 44 °C.

Stratification of Water

When a storage vessel is filled with hot water and the hot water tap is opened, the hot water is forced out of the vessel by the incoming cold water. If this incoming cold water can be

95

Fig. 6.19 Gas circulator.

kept below the hot water and prevented from mixing with it, it will be possible to draw of a large proportion of the water in the vessel as hot water. The keeping of hot and cold water inside the vessel in separate layers is termed stratification.

A tall narrow cylinder is preferable to a wide short cylinder. Great care is required when cylinders are fixed horizontally, or the cold water entering may bore up through the hot water to be deflected into the upper part of the vessel. A spreader pipe is therefore required inside the cylinder connected to the cold feed pipe. Manufacturers of electric and gas water heaters provide a baffle which

allows the cold water entering the heater to stratify at the base.

Exercises

1. State the merits and demerits of localised water-heating systems.
2. State the points that must be observed when installing electric water heaters in order to reduce the heat losses to a minimum.
3. Sketch sections and explain the working principles of the following types of electric water heater:

Fig. 6.20 Gas circulator connected to existing hot-water supply system.

(a) open outlet type,
(b) pressure type,
(c) cistern type.

4. Show by means of annotated sketches the methods of installing pressure- and cistern-types of electric water heaters in a three-storey office to supply hot water to four washbasins on each floor.

5. Sketch a section, explain the operation of an instantaneous electric water heater and show by means of sketches the method of installing the heater to supply
(a) a washbasin or sink,
(b) a shower.

6. Sketch and explain the operation of a rod-type thermostat used to control the temperature of water heated by an electric element.

7. Sketch sections and explain the operation of the following types of gas water heater:
   (a) instantaneous,
   (b) storage.
8. Define the term 'multipoint heater' and show, by means of an annotated sketch, the method of installing an instantaneous multipoint gas water heater to an existing hot water supply system. Explain how the heater may be put into use when the boiler is out.
9. Sketch and explain the operation of a gas circulator and show, by means of sketches, the methods of installing a gas circulator to
   (a) an existing hot water supply system,
   (b) a new hot water supply system where the circulator is used as the sole means of providing hot water.
10. Explain the term 'stratification of water' and show by means of a sketch how stratification is achieved in both horizontal and vertical hot water storage cylinders.
11. Explain the principles of operation of off-peak electric water heating and sketch a section of a Maxistore cylinder.

Chapter 7
Thermal Comfort
Low-Temperature Hot Water
Heating Systems

Principles

The whole problem of achieving thermal comfort of the occupants within a building is directly related to the thermal functions of the body. If the occupants are to function at maximum efficiency, their internal temperature must be controlled within certain fixed limits. Thermal controls operate within the body itself on the rate of heat production, as well as on the rate of heat flow to the external surface of the body by the rate of the flow of blood to the surface of the skin.

There are three stages of operation of internal thermal controls of the body.

1. If the body is producing heat at a rate in excess of that being lost to the internal environment, the body perspires to increase the rate of heat loss by the latent heat of evaporation of moisture from the skin.
2. If the body loses heat in excess of the rate in which it is produced, it becomes necessary to produce more heat by physical exercise, eating more food, or wearing more clothes.
3. If the rate of heat loss from the body is 'balanced' by the heat being generated in the room, a state of thermal comfort will exist.

Thermal Comfort Conditions

The problem of providing thermal comfort is therefore one of achieving a desirable heat balance between the body and its surroundings. Fig. 7.1 shows the heat losses and heat gains of a person inside a room.

The rates of heat loss from the body and the methods by which this can be controlled are as follows.

1. Radiation: 45% (approximately) controlled by the correct mean radiant temperature of the room surfaces.
2. Convection: 30% (approximately) controlled by the correct rate of air flow past the body.
3. Evaporation: 25% (approximately) controlled by the correct rate of air flow past the body and the correct relative humidity of the air.

The greatest degree of thermal comfort exists under the following room conditions:

1. when the air temperature at feet level is not greater than 3 °C below that at head level,
2. when the air flow past the body is horizontal and at a velocity of between 0.15 and 0.2 m/s a variable air velocity is preferable to a constant one and prevents monotony,
3. when the room surfaces are at or above the air temperature,
4. when the air temperature is between 16 °C and 22 °C, depending on the type of work being carried out and the

Fig. 7.1 Heat balance.

age of the occupants of the room,
5. when the relative humidity is between 40 and 60%.

Thermal Insulation

The mean radiant temperature of the external walls is an important factor in thermal comfort, and conditions are improved by good thermal insulation, which reduces heat loss from the body by radiation and of course reduces the cost of heating.

Comfort Scale

The Building Research Establishment has carried out tests on thermal comfort and produced a comfort scale similar to the one devised by Bedford; the values are established from the various tests.

Table 7.1 provides numerical values for the sensations of warmth as follows.

Low-Temperature Hot Water Heating Systems

Unless the system is required for the protec-

Table 7.1 Comfort Scale

Much too warm	7	
Too warm	6	
Comfortably warm	5	
Neither cool nor warm	4	comfort zone
Comfortably cool	3	
Too cool	2	
Much too cool	1	

tion of stored goods, the purpose is to balance the heat losses from the occupants of the building. In the system, the temperature of the hot water is kept well below boiling point, usually at a maximum of 80 °C on the flow pipe, returning at between 10 and 20 °C below this temperature.

Although water has a high specific heat capacity of approximately 4.2 kJ/kgK and is therefore more difficult to heat than other heat transfer media, e.g. air, 1.34 kJ/m³K, it can also convey more heat from the boiler to the heat emitters for the same-diameter pipe. In other words, smaller-diameter pipes may be used to convey heat by the use of water than by the use of other heat-transfer media. The higher the temperature of the water used, the smaller the diameter of pipes and heat emitters. Some of this additional

100

heat, however, will be offset by an increase in heat losses from the pipes.

Water may be circulated in the system either by means of a pump or by natural convection. Pumped circulation has now almost replaced natural convection circulation in all but the smallest installations. It has the advantage of increasing the flow rate through the pipes, which reduces the heating-up period and allows smaller diameter pipes to be used.

Open Systems. These are provided with an expansion and feed cistern, vent pipe and cold feed pipe. Various piping circuits may be used depending on the type of building and its layout.

One-Pipe Systems. These require less pipework and reduce installation costs, but the systems have the following disadvantages over the two-pipe systems.

1. The cooler water passing out of each heat emitter flows to the next one on the circuit and this results in the heat emitters at the end of the circuit being cooler than those at the beginning of the circuit. The circuit can be balanced by partially closing the lock shield valves at the beginning of the circuit.

2. The pump forces water around the main pipe but not through the heat emitters. The heat emitters are heated by natural convection due to the difference in density between the water in the branch flow pipe and the water in the branch return pipe. The heat emitters used must therefore be of the type that offers very little resistance to the flow of water. Injector tees may be used to introduce water through the heat emitters, but these increase the resistance to the flow of water through the main cirucit.

One-pipe ring systems (Fig. 7.2) are suitable for a single-storey building and the main flow pipe may be carried overhead with the return pipe at floor level.

One-pipe drop systems (Fig. 7.3) are suitable in buildings where vertical service ducts are used and the heat emitters can be placed close to them. The system permits self venting of the heat emitters.

One-pipe ladder systems (Fig. 7.4) are suitable for buildings where it is possible to run the pipes horizontal inside the room, or inside a suspended ceiling or floor duct. The heat emitters are not self venting.

One-pipe parallel systems (Fig. 7.5) are

Fig. 7.2 One-pipe ring.

Fig. 7.3 One-pipe drop.

Fig. 7.4 One-pipe ladder.

Fig. 7.5   One-pipe parallel.

similar to one-pipe ladder systems except that the return pipe is also horizontal and parallel to the flow pipe. The system is useful when it is not possible to run a vertical return pipe at the opposite end of the building to the vertical flow pipe. This may be the case when a lift shaft or a staircase is sited at the opposite end of the building to the boiler room.

Two-Pipe Systems. Although longer lengths of pipework are required for these systems, these pipes may be gradually reduced in diameter as they pass away from the boiler and gradually increased in diameter on their way back to the boiler. The cooler water from each heat emitter is carried back to the boiler by the return pipe and not passed on to the next heat emitter, as in the case of the one-pipe system. This provides a better heat balance in the system and less regulation is therefore required to even the heat distribution.

If the system is pumped, the pressure produced forces water through the heat emitters and circulation through them does not rely on natural convection, as in the case

of one-pipe systems. Heat emitters offering greater resistance to the flow of water may therefore be used with the two-pipe system, e.g. convector heaters and overhead unit heaters.

Two-pipe parallel systems (Fig. 7.6) are similar to the one-pipe parallel system, but the return pipes from each emitter are connected to the main return pipe.

Two-pipe high-level return systems (Fig. 7.7) may be used when it is impractical to install a main return pipe at low level. The system is useful when installing a heating system in an existing building having a concrete ground floor and saves the cost and inconvenience of preparing a duct for the horizontal return pipe in the concrete.

Two-pipe drop systems (Fig. 7.8) are similar to the one-pipe drop, but separate flow and return mains supply the heat emitters. The system is self venting.

Two-pipe upfeed systems (Fig. 7.9) are suitable for buildings where it is impractical to install a horizontal flow main at high level. The system is not self venting and air valves are therefore required at the top of each ver-

Fig. 7.6 Two-pipe parallel.

Fig. 7.7 Two-pipe high-level return.

Fig. 7.8 Two-pipe drop.

Fig. 7.9 Two-pipe upfeed.

tical flow pipe. The system is often used for embedded panel heating, where a panel of pipes embedded inside the floor or ceiling are used instead of separate heat emitters.

Two-pipe reverse return systems (Fig. 7.10) are also known as equal travel systems. In Fig. 7.10 the heat emitters A have a shorter flow main than heat emitters B, but it will be noticed that heat emitters A have a longer return main than heat emitters B: thus the resistance to the flow of water through the heat emitters along the horizontal run is equal, because the 'travel' is equal.

Small-Bore Heating Systems (Fig. 7.11)

This system is used extensively for houses and other small buildings. By installing a pump on either the main flow or the return pipe, it is possible to force water through small-diameter pipes, usually 15 mm or 22 mm, depending on the mass flow rate of hot water through the circuit.

One- or two-pipe circuits may be used and the hot water calorifier may be connected to the pumped circuit or provided with separate flow and return pipes which function on the natural convection principle.

Micro or Mini-bore Systems (Fig. 7.12)

This system utilises soft copper tube in coils of up to 200 m in length and with outside diameters of 6 mm, 8 mm, 10 mm or 12 mm, depending on the mass flow rate of water. These micro- or mini-bore tubes are fed from pipes having outside diameters of 28 mm or 22 mm, again depending on the mass flow rate of water. At strategic points, manifolds are inserted into these larger pipes and the micro-bore pipes are connected to these to feed the heat emitters, through either separate valves or a single double-entry valve (see Fig. 7.13). The system has the following advantages:

1. saving in installation time which can

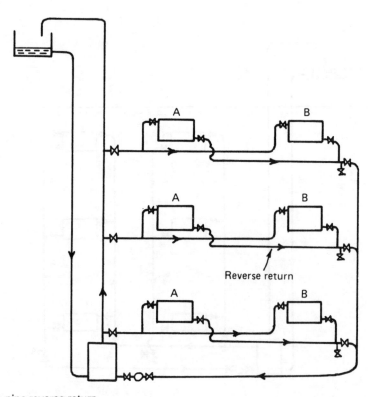

Fig. 7.10 Two-pipe reverse return.

Fig. 7.11 Small-bore heating system.

Fig. 7.12 Mini-bore or micro-bore system.

Fig. 7.13 Double entry radiator valve.

result in saving of about 15% of the capital cost of the installation,

2. micro-bore pipes are neat and easy to conceal,

3. long lengths of tubing result in fewer joints,

4. lower water content provides a quick heat recovery,

5. soft copper tends to absorb noise from the system,

6. easy cutting away of building fabric and making good,

7. spare connections on the manifolds permit extensions to the system at a later date.

Thermostatic Control of Heating Systems

The thermostatic control of the heating systems may be achieved by the following methods.

1. Zoning Valves. These are used for thermostatically control of separate circuits and the air temperature may therefore vary in each zone. In Fig. 7.11 zoning valves are shown to control the air temperatures of the rooms upstairs and downstairs.

2. Thermostatic Radiator Valves. The best comfort control and economy is achieved when each radiator is

(a) Section through valve

Packing gland

Control panel

Weather compensator

Motor

Water temperature detector

Boiler thermostat

Pump

By-pass

(b) Mixing system

Heating system

Heating system

Motor

Boiler thermostat

(c) Diverting system

Fig. 7.14 Three-way valve.

equipped with a thermostatic radiator valve. Fig. 7.12 shows a mini-bore or micro-bore heating system with thermostatic valves on each radiator and a similar valve to control the temperature of the hot water inside the calorifier.

3. Three-Way Port Valve (Fig. 7.14). These may be arranged as mixing or diverting valves. A small electric motor is connected to the valve and this is operated by a thermostat connected to the flow pipe or inside the room; external thermostats may also be used.

When operating as a mixing valve, as shown in Fig. 7.14b, cooler water from the return pipe mixes with the hotter water in the flow pipe from the boiler. This occurs when the thermostat connected to the valve responds to a rise in temperature of the water in the flow pipe, or the internal or external air. The water flowing to the heating circuit is therefore constant in volume flow rate, but variable in temperature.

When operating as a diverting valve, as shown in Fig. 7.14c, some of the hotter water in the flow pipe is diverted to the cooler water in the return pipe. This again occurs when the thermostat connected to the valve responds to a rise in temperature of the water in the flow pipe, or the internal or external air. This form of control provides a constant temperature and a variable volume flow rate.

It will be noticed by inspection of the diagrams that a mixing valve has two inlets and one outlet, whilst a diverting valve has one inlet and two outlets. Fig. 7.15 shows a fully automatic control system for a combined heating and hot water supply system using a three-way diverting valve.

The disadvantage of the three-way

Fig. 7.15 Full automatic control.

110

Fig. 7.16 Room thermostat controlling the pump.

port valve is in the fact that the method cannot take into account the different orientation or heat gains in the rooms. If an external thermostat sited on the north side of the building is used, any solar heat gains on the south side will not be taken into account. If an internal thermostat is used, the method cannot take into account other rooms, which may receive a significant amount of heat from occupants, lighting and machinery.

Thermostat Controlling the Pump (Fig. 7.16). This is the cheapest method of thermostatic control and is used extensively for houses. A room thermostat regulates the heat output from the heat emitters by switching the circulating pump on and off.

Cylinder Thermostat for Hot Water Priority (Fig. 7.17). This method provides a quick recovery of hot water temperature in the cylinder after a large quantity of hot water has been drawn off. Whenever the cylinder falls below the setting of the cylinder thermostat, the room thermostat is overridden and the pump switched off. Heating of the radiators is resumed as soon as the cylinder water temperature has recovered.

The two methods have the same disadvantage as the three-way port valve and cannot take into account the different orientations or heat gains in the rooms.

Boiler Control

The boiler must be provided with its own thermostatic control and the operating temperature must be sufficient to prevent condensation of the flue gases. The control of the boiler must also be under the influence of a time switch, which will allow the boiler to be started up and shut off at predetermined times. Alternatively, it may be required to reduce the temperature at night time, which requires an additional boiler thermostat, and the clock switch then changes over from the day thermostat to the night thermostat.

Embedded Panel Heating (Fig. 7.18)

As an alternative to the more conventional radiator systems, 15 mm or 22 mm diameter soft copper pipes may be embedded in the

Fig. 7.17 Cylinder thermostat to give priority to the hot-water supply.

Fig. 7.18 Embedded-panel heating system.

floors, walls or ceilings. This method provides an efficient form of radiant heating and a high degree of thermal comfort. The system may be used in large buildings and houses. In the system, warm water is circulated by means of a pump through panels of closely spaced pipes at 150 mm or 225 mm centres, and a three-way thermostatic mixing valve maintains the water at an even temperature. The pipes must be thoroughly tested under water pressure before being embedded.

The temperature of the water in the flow and return pipes for different panel locations is given in Table 7.2.

Solar Space Heating

Embedded heating is particularly suitable for solar space heating where solar-heated water at a comparatively low temperature may be pumped through the panels from a large insulated underground storage tank.

De-aerator (Fig. 7.19)

Pumped 'open'-type low-pressure hot water heating systems are sometimes troublesome because of water being forced through the vent pipe or air being drawn down through it. A de-aerator recently introduced by Myson Ltd. prevents the above occurrences and also allows air from the system to escape through the vent pipe. The fitting must be connected to the flow pipe and the pipework must rise to it, so that air can escape. If the fitting is connected to the horizontal flow pipe, it should be sited as close as possible to the boiler. It

must not be fitted below the level of the boiler flow pipe outlet.

The 'Combi' Combination Gas Boiler

The 'Combi' combination gas boiler requires no cistern in the roof space and no hot water storage cylinder thus saving in space and interconnecting pipework. The boiler will heat water direct from the main when a hot water tap is opened and will in addition provide efficient, fully controllable central heating. Fig. 7.20 shows the installation of the 'Combi' boiler.

The boiler is supplied with an integral expansion vessel for installation on a sealed system principle. It also has automatic ignition which saves having a pilot flame. The flue arrangement may be open, balanced or fanned. The boiler may be installed on an open principle providing that the expansion and feed cistern is fitted at 300 mm minimum above the highest point of the system.

Because the water is heated direct from the main a shower is supplied at mains water pressure which provides exhilarating showers without the use of a pump. Accurate thermostatic control of the boiler is provided by an advanced microprocessor. The boilers are available with three different outputs (known as 'Combi' 240, 280 and 350), Table 7.3 gives these details.

Exercises

1. Explain the factors that control the thermal comfort of an occupant in a room and state the usual values required to achieve the greatest degree of thermal comfort.
2. Why does good insulation increase the thermal comfort of an occupant of a room?
3. Define the term 'comfort scale' and state its values.
4. State the advantages of using water as a heating medium for a heating system.

Table 7.2 Flow and Return Temperatures

Panel location	Flow water (°C)	Return Water (°C)
Ceiling	54	43
Floor	43	35
Wall	43	35

Vent pipe

Heating flow pipe
carrying air bubbles

When the water
strikes this side
the air bubbles are
released and rise
through the vent pipe

Water stream

Flow pipe to heating system

Cold-feed pipe

(a) Section through de-areator

Expansion and
feed cistern

Vent pipe

Alternative
position of
calorifier

Air valve

Cold-
feed
pipe

De-areator

Pump

Safety valve

Hot-water
calorifier

Flow and return pipes
for heating system

Boiler

Safety valve

(b) Method of installing de-areator

Fig. 7.19   De-aerator.

Table 7.3 Outputs of 'Combi' Combination Boilers

Type of 'Combi'	Output to central heating and hot water	Output to central heating only	Output to hot water supply only	Hot water supply flow rate (litres per minute)
'Combi' 240 for apartments and small homes	9.2 — 24 kW	—	—	8.6 (40°C rise)
'Combi' 280 for small to medium sized homes	—	10.5 — 24 kW	10.5 — 28 kW	10 (40°C rise)
'Combi' 350 for medium sized family homes	—	9 — 25 kW	9 — 35kW	10 — 14 (50°C and 35°C rise respectively)

Fig. 7.20 Installation of 'Combi' combination gas boilers. Boilers are supplied by Worcester Heat Systems Ltd, Cotswold Way, Warndon, Worcester

Shower

Thermostatic control

Basin

Bath

Radiators with thermostatic valves

Thermostat in the hall

'Combi' boiler

Cold water from main

5. Describe the principles of operation of an 'open'-type water heating system.
6. Sketch the following pumped 'open' one-pipe heating systems:
   (a) ring,
   (b) drop,
   (c) ladder,
   (d) parallel.
7. State the advantages and disadvantages of a two-pipe system of heating.
8. Sketch the following pumped 'open'-type two-pipe heating systems:
   (a) parallel,
   (b) high-level return,
   (c) upfeed,
   (d) reverse return or equal travel,
   (e) downfeed or drop.
9. Describe the small-bore system of heating and show by means of an annotated isometric sketch how the system may be installed in a house having three radiators on the first floor and four radiators on the ground floor. Show on the sketch the method of providing hot water to a bath, basin and sink, by means of an indirect hot water system.
10. State the advantages of a micro- or mini-bore system of heating and sketch an isometric diagram of a system for a bungalow having four radiators.

11. Sketch and describe the following methods of thermostatic control of hot water heating systems and state the advantages of each:
    (a) thermostatic zoning valve,
    (b) thermostatic radiator valve,
    (c) three-way mixing valve,
    (d) three-way diverting valve,
    (e) switching of pump on and off.
12. Explain and illustrate by means of a sketch the method of controlling a combined heating and hot water system so that priority may be given to the supply of hot water.
13. Sketch and describe an embedded panel system of heating and sketch a section through the following structures to show the method of embedding the pipes:
    (a) concrete ground floor,
    (b) ceiling constructed of concrete,
    (c) ceiling constructed of joists and plasterboard.
14. Show by means of a sketch and explain the operation of a de-aerator for a pumped hot water heating system.
15. Sketch a diagram of the 'Combi' system of heating and hot water supply and state its advantages over a conventional system.

116

Chapter 8
Heat Loss Calculations, Heat Emitters

Definition of Terms

Thermal Conductivity (k) (Table 8.1). In SI units, the thermal conductivity is expressed as the heat flow, in watts per square metre of surface area of a material, for a temperature difference of 1 °C per metre thickness and may be expressed as

$$\frac{W\ m}{m^2 K}$$

The thickness divided by the area m/m² cancels to 1/m and the expression results in W/m K.

Thermal Resistivity (r). This is also a property of a material, regardless of its size or thickness. It is the reciprocal of the conductivity. The unit is

$$m\ K/W$$

Note: in this case m²/m cancels to m.

Thermal Resistance (R). This is a product of the thermal resistivity and thickness (L/k) and is expressed as

$$m^2\ K/W$$

Note: if the thickness, L, is quoted in millimetres it must be converted into metres.

Thermal Transmittance (U). This is the property of a structure depending on the thickness of the material, and is a measure of its ability to transmit heat. It is defined as the quantity of heat that will flow through a unit area, in unit time, per unit difference of temperature between the inside and outside environment. It is calculated as the reciprocal of the sum of the resistances of each layer of construction and the resistances of the inner and outer surfaces and of any air space or cavity. It is expressed as

$$W/m^2\ K$$

Table 8.1   Thermal Conductivities

Material	k value
Brickwork	
light	0.80
average	1.20
dense	1.50
Concrete	
dense	1.40
aerated	0.14
Clinker block	0.05
Glass wool	0.034
Plaster	
gypsum	0.40
vermiculite	0.20
Rendering (cement and sand)	0.53
Slates	1.50
Stone	
limestone	1.50
sandstone	1.30
Timber	
softwood	0.14
hardwood	0.16

Calculation of U Values

For a simple structure the thermal transmission is expressed as

$$U = \frac{1}{R_{si} + R_{so} + R_a + R_1 + R_2 + R_3}$$

where R_{si} is the inside surface resistance, R_{so} is the outside surface resistance, R_a is the resistance of the air space, and R_1 R_2 and R_3 are resistances of structural components. Since the thermal resistance, R, is L/k, the expression may also be given as

$$U = \frac{1}{R_{si} + R_{so} + R_a + \frac{L_1}{k_1} + \frac{L_2}{k_2} + \frac{L_3}{k_3}}$$

(see Fig. 8.1). Table 8.1 gives the thermal conductivity of some common building materials.

Surface Resistances

The standard values for the internal surface resistances are given in Table 8.2.

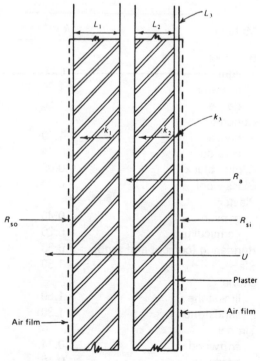

Fig. 8.1 Thermal values.

118

Table 8.2 Internal Surface Resistances

Internal surface resistance (R_{si})	m² K/W
Walls	0.12
Floors	0.15
Ceilings	0.11

Table 8.3 External Surface Resistance (R_{so}), m² K/W

Building element	Surface emissivity	Exposure		
		Sheltered	Standard	Severe
Wall	High	0.080	0.053	0.027
	Low	0.106	0.062	0.027
Roof	High	0.070	0.044	0.018
	Low	0.088	0.053	0.018

In the past, the values used for the external surface resistances of walls have been varied according to their orientation. The Building Research Establishment (BRE) suggest that the values should instead take into account the degree of exposure as given in Table 8.3. In column two of Table 8.3, the emissivity should be taken as high for all common building materials, including glass. Unpainted or untreated metal surfaces, such as aluminium or galvanised steel, should be taken as having low emissivity. The exposure categories should be taken as follows:

1. Sheltered. The first two storeys above ground of buildings in the interior of towns.
2. Normal. The third to the fifth storeys of buildings in the interior of towns and most suburban and country buildings.
3. Severe. The sixth and higher floors of buildings in the interior of towns and buildings exposed on hill sites, coasts and riversides.

The standard thermal resistances of unventilated air spaces are given in Table 8.4.

Example 8.1. Calculate the U value for the external wall of the house shown in Fig. 8.2.

Table 8.4 Thermal Resistances of Unvented Air Spaces

Type of air space		Thermal resistance m² K/W	
Thickness (mm)	Surface emissivity	Heat flow horizontal	Heat flow down wards or upwards
5	high	0.11	0.11
	low	0.18	0.18
20	high	0.18	0.21
	low	0.35	1.06

(Thermal conductivities: brickwork, 1.20 W/m K; clinker block, 0.14 W/m K; plaster, 0.40 W/m K. Thermal resistances: inside surface, 0.120 m² K/W; outside surface, 0.053 m² K/W; cavity, 0.180 m² K/W.)

$$U = \cfrac{1}{R_{si} + R_{so} + R_a + \cfrac{L_1}{k_1} + \cfrac{L_2}{k_2} + \cfrac{L_3}{k_3}}$$

$$= \cfrac{1}{[0.12 + 0.053 + 0.18 + (0.121/1.20) + (0.08/0.14) + (0.02/0.40)]}$$

$$= \frac{1}{1.073}$$

$$= 0.93 \ \text{W/m}^2 \ \text{K}$$

Although it is very useful to calculate the U values of a structure, and this may be necessary in certain cases, their values are often given by various authorities. Table 8.5 gives a list of U values, which is part of a table in the Institute of Plumbing Guide Book.

Heat Loss due to Infiltration of Air

To find the heat loss by ventilation or infiltration of air, the following formula may be used:

20 mm thickness of plaster

U value 0.93 W/m²K

80 mm thickness of clinker block

50 mm · wide unvented cavity

121 mm thickness of brickwork

Fig. 8.2 U value for cavity wall, Example 8.1.

$$Qv = \frac{H\,C \times V \times (t_i - t_o) \times N}{3600} \quad \text{(W)}$$

where Qv is the heat loss in W, $H\,C$ is the heat capacity of air (1340 J/m³ K), V is the volume of room in m³, t_i is the air temperature inside, t_o is the air temperature outside, and N is the number of air changes per hour. This formula is often required for answers to examination questions, but for practical purposes the following formula may be used:

$$Qv = 0.33\,N\,V\,(t_i - t_o) \quad \text{(W)}$$

where Qv is the heat loss in W, N is the number of air changes per hour, V is the volume of room in m³, t_i is the temperature inside, and t_o is the temperature outside.

Heat Loss Calculations

When the thermal transmissions (U values) of the various elements of a structure and the ventilation rates are known, it is possible to estimate the total heat losses from a building. In any building where the air temperature inside is higher than that outside, heat loss will occur by conduction through the building fabric and by interchange of the inside and outside air. These two forms of heat loss may

Table 8.5　Heat Losses through Building Fabric (U Values), W/m² K

Construction	Average	Exposed	Construction	Average	Exposed
External Walls			75 mm breeze, plastered both sides	2.25	—
Brickwork, solid, plastered 121 mm	3.00	3.30			
Brickwork, solid, plastered 236 mm	2.10	2.30	*Flat Roofs*		
			3-layer felt on strawboard joists and plasterboard	1.05	1.08
Cavity Walls, plastered			Asphalt on 104 mm concrete and plaster ceiling	3.41	3.75
Both leaves 105 mm brick	1.50	1.65	Asphalt on 150 mm concrete and plaster ceiling	3.12	3.48
Outer leaf 121 mm brick, inner leaf 104 mm insulated concrete plus 25 mm insulating board in cavity	0.60	0.70			
			Pitched Roofs		
Windows			Tiles on battens and felt	2.75	3.02
Single-glazing, wood frames	4.30	4.73	Plaster ceiling, roof space above with 100 mm glass fibre		
Double-glazing, wood frames	2.80	2.75	between joists	0.35	0.57
Single-glazing, metal frames	5.60	6.16			
Double-glazing, metal frames	3.20	3.52	*Ground Floors*		
			Ventilated wood floors on joists	0.61	—
Partition Walls			Solid floors	0.36	—
121 mm brick, plastered both sides	2.30	—			

be referred to as fabric heat loss and ventilation heat loss. To maintain any required temperature conditions inside the building, the rate of heat imput must be equal to the rate of heat loss. The fabric heat losses may be estimated from the following equation:

$$\text{Heat loss} = A \times U \times (t_i - t_o) \quad \text{(W)}$$

where A is the area of each element of the structure in m², U is the thermal transmission through the fabric in W/m² K, t_i is the temperature of the air inside, in °C, and t_o is the temperature of the air outside, in °C. An example will show how these heat losses are estimated.

Example 8.2　Figs 8.3 and 8.4 show the ground floor and first floor plans of a small detached house. Estimate the heat losses from the lounge and bedroom one, assuming that the outside air temperature is −1 °C, there are two air changes per hour, and the

rooms are 2.4 m high and have windows sized 1.7 m × 1.4 m. Use the following U values (in W/m² K).

Lounge

ground floor	0.30
external walls	0.40
internal wall	2.25
door	2.30
windows (double glazed)	2.80
ceiling	0.30

Bedroom 1

external walls	0.40
window (double glazed)	2.80
ceiling	0.20

Note: in the lounge there will be no heat loss into the dining room, so this inner wall will be ignored. In the bedroom there will be a heat gain through the floor from the lounge; and there will be no heat loss through the inner walls so these can be ignored.

An estimate of the heat loss through the fabric can now be made (Tables 8.6 and 8.7).

120

Table 8.6 Heat Loss through Fabric of Lounge

Type of fabric	Area (m²)	U Value (Wm² K)	Temperature difference (°C)	Total heat loss (W)
Ground floor	18	0.30	22	118.8
External walls (less windows)	(20.4−4.76) = 15.64	0.40	22	137.63
Internal wall (less door)	(10.8−1.52) = 9.28	2.25	3	62.64
Windows	4.76	2.80	22	293.22
Door	1.52	2.30	3	10.49
Ceiling	18	0.20	5	18.00
				640.78

Ventilation loss Qv = 0.33 Nv $(t_1−t_0)$
$\quad\quad\quad\quad\quad$ = 0.33 × 2 × 43.2 × 22
$\quad\quad\quad\quad\quad$ = 627.26
Total heat loss $\quad$ = 627.26 + 640.78
$\quad\quad\quad\quad\quad\quad$ = 1268.04 W

Table 8.7 Heat Loss through Fabric Bedroom 1

Type of fabric	Area (m²)	U Value (Wm² K)	Temperature difference (°C)	Total heat loss (W)
External walls (less windows)	(20.4−4.76) = 15.6	0.40	17	106.08
Windows	4.76	2.80	17	226.58
Ceiling	18	0.20	17	61.12
				393.78
Less heat gain through floor	18	0.20	5	18.00
				375.78

Ventilation loss Qv = 0.33 Nv $(t_1−t_0)$
$\quad\quad\quad\quad\quad$ = 0.33 × 2 × 43.2 × 17
$\quad\quad\quad\quad\quad$ = 484.70
Total heat loss $\quad$ = 484.70 + 375.78
$\quad\quad\quad\quad\quad\quad$ = 860.48 W

Fig. 8.3 Ground floor plan.

Area of Radiators

Allowing for a heat emission from the radiator of 520 W/m² in the lounge and 530 W/m² in bedroom one, the areas of the radiators will be as follows. For lounge,

$$\text{Area} = \frac{1268.046}{520}$$

$$= 2.44 \text{ m}^2$$

Two radiators each 1.22m² in area, will be required and these will be fixed below the windows. For bedroom 1,

$$\text{Area} = \frac{860.48}{530}$$

$$= 1.62 \text{ m}^2$$

Two radiators, each 0.81 m² in area, will be required and these again will be fixed below the windows.

Note: the higher temperature difference between the air and the surface of the radiator in bedroom one will result in a higher heat emission, hence 530 W/m² instead of 520 W/m². The student should calculate the radiator areas for the other rooms.

122

Building Regulations
Conservation of Fuel and Power

The requirements for dwellings are as follows:

1. The calculated rate of heat loss (WK) through any windows and roof lights shall be no greater than it would be if:

(a) the aggregate of the areas of windows and roof lights do not exceed 20 percent of the total floor area, and

(b) the windows and roof lights had a *U* value of 3.3.

2. The calculated rate of heat loss through the solid parts of the exposed elements shall not be greater than it would be if:

Fig. 8.4 First floor plan.

(a) the exposed walls and exposed floors had a U value of 0.45 and

(b) the roof had a U value of 0.25.

3. The extent that the calculated rate of heat loss through the solid parts of exposed elements is less than the maximum permitted under sub-paragraph (2) the calculated rate of heat loss through windows and roof lights may be greater than the maximum permitted under paragraph (1).

Boiler Power

The sum of the heat losses from the various rooms will give the boiler power required in watts for the heating system and to this must be added the power required to heat the domestic hot water. A 10% margin may then be added to this total to allow for exceptionally cold weather.

Heat Emitters

Various types of heat emitter are available to suit different conditions of heating. Some types operate on convection and others on radiation, or a combination of both.

Convection. Convected heat directly warms the surrounding air and is distributed throughout the room by convection currents. Convection currents move in an upward direction, being displaced by the cooler denser air. Convected heat has the advantage of carrying heat around obstacles, which would limit the transmission of radiant heat.

Radiation. Radiant heat is transmitted from a heat emitter in straight lines and passes through the air in the form of heat waves. It is only when these waves strike an opaque surface that they are felt as heat. Radiant heat is directional, which means that a radiant heater can be placed so that it radiates heat to selected areas of a room. This heat, however, can be interrupted by an opaque body placed in its path.

Radiant heat has the following advantages:

1. The walls and contents of a room are kept relatively warm and the heat loss from the occupants is consequently lower.
2. The air temperature is lower which is more conducive to physical and mental activity.
3. The lower air temperature results in about 15% saving in fuel costs.
4. Draughts are reduced to a minimum.
5. When radiant heat warms the surfaces on which they strike, some convected heat is transmitted from them.

Column Radiators (Fig. 8.5). Most of the heat from this type of emitter is transmitted by convection. The emitter provides a great deal of surface area, which increases its heat output.

Hospital Radiators (Fig. 8.6). This type of emitter contains fewer dust traps and is therefore more hygienic, hence its use in hospitals. The heat transmitted from the emitter is again mainly by convection.

Panel Radiators (Fig. 8.7). Because of their greater plane surface area, these emitters transmit most of the heat by radiation. Pressed steel panel radiators are

Fig. 8.5   Column-type radiator.

Fig. 8.6   Hospital-pattern radiator.

Fig. 8.7   Panel-type radiator.

extremely popular for domestic heating systems.

Skirting Convectors (Fig. 8.8). These consist of a continuous finned heating pipe enclosed inside a sheet metal casing. They provide excellent heat distribution by convection. When installing these heat emitters, care must be taken to ensure that the gap at the base is not closed by the carpet, or the

efficiency of the emitters will be drastically reduced.

Radiant Skirting Heaters (Fig. 8.9). These help to reduce cold draughts at floor level whilst still providing radiant heat at higher level.

Natural Convectors (Fig. 8.10). These consist of a finned heater placed at low level inside a metal casing. If required, a damper may be incorporated inside the heater to control the flow of air through the emitter. A tall heater will transmit more convected heat than a short heater.

Finned heater

Fig. 8.8   Skirting convector.

Fig. 8.9   Radiant skirting heater.

Fig. 8.10   Natural convector.

Fan Convectors (Fig. 8.11). These consist of a finned heater, usually placed in the top of a metal casing, with a fan or fans placed at the bottom, below the heater. The fan or fans may be two- or three-speed types and the control of the heat output from the emitter may be achieved by altering the speed of the fan or fans.

These emitters have the advantage over natural convectors of providing quicker heating of the air in the room and of providing better heat distribution. The additional cost of running the fan or fans must, however, be taken into account.

Overhead Unit Heaters (Fig. 8.12). These again consist of a finned heat exchanger inside a metal casing, with a fan to force air

Fig. 8.11   Fan convector.

Fig. 8.12 Overhead unit heater.

through the heater onto the working plane. The adjustable louvres may be arranged to direct the warm air where it is required. The emitters may be used during the summer months to circulate the air in the room, when the heater is switched off.

Radiant Panels (Fig. 8.13). These consist of a pipe coil inside a flat metal casing. The flat metal surface ensures that maximum radiant heat is transmitted from the emitter. They are available in a wide range of heights and lengths, and may be mounted on the wall or ceiling, flush to the finished plaster.

Radiant Strips (Fig. 8.14). These are formed from a combination of exposed pipes and sheet metal plates with an insulated back. They may be arranged in continuous runs of up to about 30 m and may be installed in workshops or warehouses.

Positions of Radiators

If a radiator is placed under a window, as shown in Fig. 8.15a, the rising stream of air mixes with the incoming cold air from the window. This provides a good distribution of warm air inside the room and reduces cold draughts at floor level and cold spots near the window.

If a radiator is placed on the wall opposite a window, as shown in Fig. 8.15b, the cold air from the window will flow downwards and across the floor. This will cause cold draughts at floor level. Greater thermal comfort will therefore result by placing radiators below the windows.

Painting of Radiators

The paint applied to the surfaces of radiators and panels does not effect their efficiency as convectors, but it can substantially reduce the

Fig. 8.13 Radiant panel heater.

Insulation

Heating pipe

Radiant heat

Fig. 8.14   Radiant strip.

amount of heat transmitted by radiation.

The best radiating surface at high temperature is matt black paint. Research by various authorities, however, has shown that the

(a) Under the window

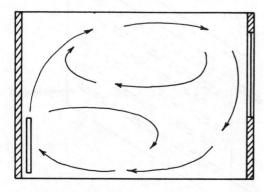

(b) On inside wall opposite the window

Fig. 8.15   Positions of radiators.

radiant heat emitted from various painted surfaces (gloss or matt), including green, red and white, is much the same below a temperature of 100 °C.

Metallic paints, such as aluminium, bronze or gold, may reduce radiation by as much as 90%, although convected heat remains unaffected.

Exercises

1. Define
    (a) thermal conductivity,
    (b) thermal resistivity,
    (c) thermal resistance,
    (d) thermal transmittance.

2. Calculate the thermal transmittance (U value) of a solid brick wall 105 mm thick, using the following values:
    external surface
    resistance = 0.053 m² K/W,
    internal surface
    resistance = 0.123 m² K/W,
    thermal conductivity
    of brick = 1.20 W/m K.

3. Calculate the thermal transmittance (U value) of an external wall of a house, using the following values:

	Thermal conductivities (W/m K)	Thickness (mm)
brickwork	1.2	110

aerated concrete block	0.14	75
plaster	0.4	20

Thermal resistances

inside surface	0.120 m² °K/W
outside surface	0.053 m² °K/W
cavity	0.180 m² °K/W

4. Calculate the heat required to ventilate a room measuring 6 m long × 3 m wide × 2.5 m high, when the air changes are three per hour and the inside and outside air temperatures are 20 °C and −1 °C respectively.

5. A room measuring 5 m long × 4 m wide × 2.5 m high has two windows each measuring 1.8 m wide × 1.2 m high and a door measuring 1 m wide × 2 m high. A room adjoining one of the long sides will be heated to 18 °C and the other three sides are to be external walls. The windows are to be in the external walls and the door in the internal wall.

   The room is to be heated to a temperature of 22 °C when the outside air temperature is −1 °C. Calculate, using the following data, the heat losses in W and the area of the radiators in m².

   U values (W/m² K)

external walls	0.96
internal wall	2.25
windows	2.80
door	2.30
ceiling	0.90
floor	0.36

air change	$1\frac{1}{2}$ per hour
heat capacity of air	1340 J/m³ K
radiator heat emission	540 W/m²

6. Explain how a room is heated (a) by convection and (b) by radiation, and state the advantages of these methods of heat transfer.

7. Sketch the following types of heat emitter and explain their operation:
   (a) skirting convector,
   (b) natural convector,
   (c) fan convector,
   (d) radiant panel,
   (e) overhead unit heater.

8. Explain why a heat emitter sited below a window is preferable to a heat emitter sited on an inside wall opposite a window.

9. What effect would the painting of radiators, by various types and colours of paint, have on the heat transmission from the radiators?

Chapter 9
Sealed Heating Systems (Unvented)

Principles

In any water heating system, provision must be made for the expansion of water. In the open system described in Chapter 7, an expansion and feed cistern is required. This cistern requires a ballvalve and overflow pipe and must be large enough to accommodate the expanded water plus a margin of $33\frac{1}{3}\%$ for extreme cold weather, when the water temperature will be higher and expansion greater.

The open system also requires an open vent and cold feed pipes, so care has to be taken in the location of the pump, or water may be forced out of the vent pipe or air drawn through it. If air is drawn into the system through the vent pipes, air locks may result and there is a greater risk of corrosion of the boiler and radiators.

The water in the cistern is also in contact with the atmospheric air, which results in its evaporation and entry of air into the system, which again may cause corrosion in the system.

Flexible-Membrane Expansion Vessel (Fig. 9.1)

In the sealed (often named 'unvented') system of heating, the open expansion and feed cistern is replaced by a flexible-membrane expansion vessel. The vessel is fitted near the boiler, either on the flow or return pipe. The vessel may also be piped away from the boiler by the following pipe sizes:

up to 24 kW,   15 mm diameter
above 24 kW,   22 mm diameter

The vessel is divided into two compartments by means of a rubber diaphragm. One side of the diaphragm is filled with nitrogen gas and the other is connected to the heating system and thus filled with water. To support the static head produced by the height of the water in the system, the nitrogen gas is pressurised so as to produce a minimum water pressure at the highest point on the circuit of 10 kPa.

Size of Expansion Vessel

The expansion vessel must be sized so that its volume is at least equal to the volume of expansion of water in the system, when raised from 10 °C to 110 °C, irrespective of the normal working temperature. Table 9.1 may be used for calculating the approximate size of the vessel.

System Characteristics

The system should conform to the *Heating and Ventilating Contractors Association Guide to Good Practice; Smallbore and Microbore Domestic Central Heating, Part 2, Sealed Systems*. The expansion vessel should meet the requirements of BS 4814: Expansion Vessels in Sealed Hot Water Systems.

Nitrogen gas cushion

Metal sphere

Flexible diaphragm

Water expanded from heating system

Connection to sealed heating system

Before connecting to heating system

After connecting to heating system

Connection to sealed heating system

Water expanded from heating system

Flexible diaphragm

Metal cylinder

Nitrogen gas cushion

Fig. 9.1 Expansion vessels.

Table 9.1 Approximate Sizes of Expansion Vessels

System load (kW)	Nominal vessel size (litres)	
	Traditional boiler and radiators	Low content boilers and fan convectors
3	4	4
6	4	4
12	8	4
18	12	8
24	18	8

The size of the system is limited to a heating load of 45 kW, but the general installation principles, given below, apply equally to much larger systems. The essentials of the HVCA Code and the British Standard are summarised as follows:

Maximum flow temperature, 99 °C
Temperature drop in the circuit, 8–17 °C
Maximum boiler working pressure, 300 kPa
Pressure relief valve blow off pressure 30 kPa above maximum working pressure
Minimum pressure at highest point on the circuit, 10 kPa
Maximum water velocity in the circuit, 1.5 m/s

Safety Devices

1. Pressure relief valve with non-metallic disc and metal seat with discharge pipe in a visible but safe place where there is no risk of contact with the hot water by persons using the building. The discharge should be via an air break to a tun dish.
2. Automatic controls and limit devices, on the heat or energy input, so designed as to ensure that the water temperature is controlled so as not to exceed 100 °C.
3. Thermal relief valve set to open should the water temperature exceed 100 °C. The valve should be connected to a discharge pipe as described in part 1.
4. Pressure gauge and thermometer fixed to the boiler or connecting pipe.

Hot-Water Cylinder

The primary heating element of the cylinder should be rated at 35 kPa higher than the relief valve setting. The heat recovery time for the water when heated from 10 °C to 66 °C should be 2 h. If the primary circuit to the cylinder operates on natural convection, the diameter of the pipes should not be less than 22 mm.

Advantages of the Sealed System

Apart from the cost saving brought about by not having to install an expansion and feed cistern in the roof and provide all the necessary pipe connections, the system has the following merits.

1. Being a sealed system, there is less risk of oxygen entering the system.
2. Pumping over or drawing air through the vent pipe is eliminated.
3. Noise due to bubble formation in the boiler or gas-fired heat exchanger is eliminated because of the increased water pressure.
4. The boiler may operate at a higher temperature, thus reducing the areas of the radiators and diameters of pipes.
5. The boiler may be sited on the roof, thus reducing the length of the flue and saving valuable space at the lower level.

Layout of the System

Fig. 9.2 shows a system incorporating a combined expansion vessel, pressure gauge, automatic air valve and pressure-relief unit. The unit will save a good deal of installation time.

Fig. 9.3 shows a combined heating and hot water supply system supplied with cold water from a top-up bottle. A non-return valve in the cold feed pipe prevents hot water flowing into the bottle from the heating system.

Fig. 9.4 shows a sealed micro-bore system with a rooftop boiler room. Several radiators may be connected to the manifolds by means of 6, 8, 10 or 12 mm bore soft copper pipes.

Heat Emitters

Radiators or convector heaters may be used for the system, but the temperature of any exposed part should be at a maximum of 82 °C, or there will be a danger to the occupants.

Filling and Commissioning the System

The system may be filled by a top-up bottle or direct from the water main using a flexible hose, providing a non-return valve and stop valve is incorporated. The system may also be filled by means of a force pump drawing water from a cistern. Sealed systems may require topping up with water in the first few months of operation.

In commissioning the system, it is generally advisable to maintain a low pressure and high temperature for a period of a few hours, to assist the elimination of air. When the system cools down, the system should be adjusted to

Flow and return pipes to hot water cylinder and heating system

Pump

Pressure relief valve

Automatic air valve

Air purger

Pressure gauge

Boiler

Drain valve

Filling valve

Expansion vessel

Air

Water

Section through air purger

Fig. 9.2 Combined expansion vessel, pressure gauge, automatic air valve and pressure relief valve unit.

Fig. 9.3 Combined heating and hot-water supply sealed system.

134

Rooftop boiler room

Double entry radiator valve

Radiator

Manifold

Flow and return mains

Micro-bore pipes

Fig. 9.4 Sealed micro-bore system with rooftop boiler room.

135

a value equal to the static head, plus a margin of 50 kPa. The final pressure at maximum temperature, and with all the heat emitters and circuits in operation, should not exceed 300 kPa.

Example 9.1. Calculate the pressure of gas in the expansion vessel when the static head above the vessel is 5 m and the water is cool.

Pressure
required
$$= \text{(Head in metres} \times 9.81) + 50$$
$$= (5 \times 9.81) + 50$$
$$= 99 \text{ kPa}$$
$$(100 \text{ kPa approx.})$$

Location of the Expansion Vessel

In siting the expansion vessel, consideration should be given to its position in relation to the position of the pump. The vessel should never be connected to the positive side of the pump, or the pump pressure will act on the rubber diaphragm and be added to the system water pressure.

The vessel may be connected to either the flow or return pipe, but, because the vessel diaphragm is manufactured from rubber, connecting it to the return pipe would provide cooler water and thus increase the life of the rubber. Fig. 9.5 shows a small combined heating and hot water supply system with the expansion vessel connected to the return pipe. The three-way diverting valve will control the temperatures of both the hot water supply and the heating system.

For larger systems operating at higher temperatures, it is advisable to connect the expansion vessel to a separate pipe and site the vessel away from the boiler.

Fig. 9.6 shows a system with an expansion vessel fixed to the wall and connected to the boiler by a noncirculating pipe. To avoid thermal circulation in the pipe, a vertical anti-gravity loop should be included and any isolating valve fixed on the pipe should be locked to prevent accidently closing and disconnecting the boiler from the vessel.

Fig. 9.5 Small sealed combined heating and hot-water supply system.

Fig. 9.6 Expansion vessel with anti-gravity loop.

Fig. 9.7 shows a sealed system for a larger building, with two expansion vessels and a boiler feed cistern and pump. The pressure cut-out switches are wired in series with the boiler-burner control circuit to isolate the plant electrically in the event of excess pressure fluctuation. The operation of the switches must not affect the function of the expansion vessels.

Exercises

1. Explain the principles of operation of a sealed heating system and state its advantages over an open heating system.
2. Sketch a section through an expansion vessel and state the method of finding the volume of the vessel for a heating system.
3. State the maximum and minimum water pressures used in a sealed heating system and the maximum flow water temperature from the boiler.
4. Describe the safety devices required for a sealed heating system and explain their operation.
5. Sketch an elevation of a boiler showing the position of the following fittings:
   (a) expansion vessel,
   (b) automatic air valve,
   (c) air purger,
   (d) pressure relief valve,
   (e) drain valve,
   (f) pressure gauge,

Fig. 9.7 Sealed system for larger building.

(g) filling valve.

6. Sketch an annotated isometric diagram of a sealed, combined heating and hot water supply system suitable for a three-bedroomed house having three radiators upstairs and downstairs respectively.

7. Sketch an elevation of a sealed heating system for a three-storey office block when the boiler is to be sited on the roof, showing all pipework and fittings.

8. Explain the operation of a top-up bottle in a sealed heating system.

9. Describe the method of filling and commissioning a sealed heating system.

10. Calculate the pressure of gas inside an expansion vessel when the head of water above the vessel is 8 m. A margin of 50 kPa above the static head pressure is required.

11. State the best location in the heating system for the expansion vessel and the reasons for using this position.

12. Sketch the installation of two large boilers used for a large sealed heating system showing expansion vessels, boiler feed cistern and pump. Explain the operation of the boiler plant.

Chapter 10
Warm Air Heating Systems

Warm air heating systems are of two main types: natural circulation and forced circulation.

Natural Circulation Systems

This type of system has not been popular in the UK, but it has been widely used in North America and some European Countries. It is generally suitable only for houses where there is a basement, so that the heated air can flow through the ductwork by natural convection created by the stack pressure. The air is heated by a furnace, which forms a direct heat exchanger, and this unit should be sited in a central position so that the duct lengths are reduced to a minimum.

Because the warm air flows through the ductwork by natural convection, the movement and pressure of the air as it enters the room is very small. The system, therefore, is easily affected by any positive pressure inside the rooms due to air infiltration from outside. One type of natural circulation employs a convector heater placed in a central position. The system is suitable for open-plan houses and bungalows and the heater may be fitted with a radiant panel to provide both radiant and convective heating. An advantage claimed for the natural circulation system is the absence of a fan, which uses electrical power and may give rise to noise problems.

Forced Circulation Systems

A more complex system of ductwork requires forced circulation, because a fan must be used to overcome the frictional resistances in the ductwork. The system may be 'direct', with the airflow over a combustion chamber, or 'indirect', with the airflow over a water-heated heat exchanger.

Direct Systems. Figs. 10.1, 10.2 and 10.3 show diagrammatic sections of gas, oil and solid-fuel direct air heaters. The gas and oil heaters required either a gas circulator or an electric immersion heater to heat the water in the cylinder. The direct system has advantages of:
1. very rapid heating up,
2. cost — it is usually cheaper,
3. lower resistance to airflow,
4. the outlet temperature may be higher,
5. no risk of freezing;
and disadvantages that
1. except for special types, they cannot provide hot water supply,
2. most units can be controlled only on the on/off or high/low principle,
3. because a flue is required, it is not always possible to site the unit in a central position.

Indirect Systems. Fig. 10.4 shows a diagrammatic section through an indirect air heater; the boiler also heats the hot water supply cylinder. An indirect system has the advantages that
1. it can be used with any type of boiler,
2. the boiler can also heat the water in the cylinder,

Fig. 10.1 Gas air heater.

Flue pipe

Warm-air plenum

Outer casing

Heat exchanger

Burner

Fan

Filter

Return-air plenum

Flue

Warm-air plenum

Combustion chamber

Return-air plenum

Flame

Pressure jet burner

Fan

Fig. 10.2 Oil-fired air heater.

Fig. 10.3 Combined solid-fuel air and water heater.

3. it can be sited in a central position,
4. if the unit is sited inside the roof space there is no risk of fire,
5. the water temperature can be variable;

and the disadvantages that

1. it is usually more costly,
2. there is risk of freezing when the house is left unoccupied during the winter.
3. there are additional heat losses from the pipes supplying the heater,
4. the air outlet temperature is lower and the heating-up period is therefore longer,
5. because the temperature of the heat exchanger is lower, the heating unit must be larger, which takes up more space.

System Layout

The layout of the system depends on the positions of the warm air inlets and outlets, and the heating unit, and these depend on the layout of the building.

The ductwork systems fall into the following patterns. When the heater is sited in the centre of the building, an extended plenum or a radial system may be used (see

Silent fan

Return-air plenum

Flow pipe

Filter

Return pipe

Finned copper heat exchanger

Warm-air plenum

Section through heater

Vent →

Alternative position of heater (or top of airing cupboard)

Cylinder →

Air valve

Thermostatic valve

Heater in central position

Isolating valve

Boiler

Fig. 10.4 Indirect air heater.

142

Figs. 10.5, 10.6 and 10.7). These systems ensure that the lengths of the individual ducts to the rooms are reduced to the minimum, thus minimising the frictional resistance. They also provide a better balance of air flow to each room. If the heater has to be sited at one end of the building, a stepped duct system is required as shown in Fig. 10.8. The air inlets should be sited either above or below the windows, so that a warm air curtain will flow past the windows and thus prevent the entering cold air from flowing along the floor.

Stub Duct System (Fig. 10.9)

To save on installation costs, the warm air heater may be sited in the centre of the room to be heated and short or stub ducts from the

Fig. 10.5   Extended-plenum system.

Fig. 10.6   Radial duct system with ceiling inlets.

Fig. 10.7 Radial system with floor inlets.

Floor diffuser
225 mm from
inside wall

Heater

Fig. 10.8 Stepped-duct system.

Heater

Floor diffuser

Stepped duct

Kitchen

Dining room

Return air
grill in top
of door

Heater

Stub duct

Hall

Lounge

Fig. 10.9 Stub duct system (plan).

heater taken through to the inside walls. This method is very common in flats, but from the thermal comfort standard, however, the warm air should undoubtedly be distributed from around the outside walls, i.e. perimeter heating.

Modulated Air and Heat Output (Fig. 10.10)

A recent development in gas warm air heating using stub ducts is the use of a control system, which modulates both heat and air output to match the heat demand, resulting in a continuous flow of warm air at a constant temperature. If fresh air is drawn into the heating system via a duct and its volume is controlled by a special stabiliser, a mechanical ventilation system can be achieved. Ventilation will be draught free, as all the air will be heated before distribution. When no heating is required, the air-circulating fan of the air

heater operates at a minimum speed to maintain continuous ventilation. The system operates as follows. Fresh air from the ventilated roof space passes through a bird cage (A) and enters the ventilating stabiliser (B), which draws balancing air from the house via the ceiling grille (C). Duct D carries air to the plenum chamber (E), which is connected to the recirculation grille (F).

For summer-boost ventilation, a switch operates damper G to open a special fresh air duct (H) and cut off air from recirculating grille F. The fan then operates at top speed.

Return Air

Whenever possible, the return air outlet should be opposite the warm air inlet. Several different combinations are possible.

1. With the inlet below the windows, the return air outlet should be sited on the

Fig. 10.10   Stub duct system with modulated air and heat output.

opposite wall just below the ceiling, or in the ceiling itself.

2. With the inlet above the windows, the return air outlet should be sited on the opposite wall just above the skirting level.

For domestic work, one main return air duct is usually sufficient and the duct can be carried through from the inside wall of the hall to the heater. The return air from the rooms is drawn back to the hall, where it passes through the duct to the heater. With this method, it is necessary to provide either sufficient space below the doors for the return air or a grille on the walls opposite the inlets.

Fresh Air

It is good practice to allow for some admixture of fresh air from the outside with the return air, and the fresh air duct should be large enough to provide about 25% of the total air requirement. Difficulty sometimes exist where, because of the wind, warm air is extracted instead of fresh air entering. This can be overcome by providing two fresh air inlets from opposite walls at right angles to each other, and bringing the two together in a 'balancing chamber' from which fresh air is taken into the return air duct. Another method of overcoming this problem is to fit a draught stabiliser on the fresh air duct.

In these days of ever-increasing fuel costs, fresh air admixture is sometimes omitted and fresh air brought in by natural infiltration through doors and windows. With either method, it is essential that there is always in adequate supply of air for combustion at the heater.

Figs. 10.11, 10.12 and 10.13 show ceiling, floor and wall inlets respectively. The same type of fitting show in Figs. 10.11 and 10.13 may also be used for outlets.

Ductwork

The ductwork may be circular, rectangular or

Fig. 10.11   Ceiling inlet.

Fig. 10.12   Floor inlet.

Fig. 10.13   Wall inlet.

square, and made from galvanised sheet steel or plastic. The following principles in designing the ductwork should be observed.

1. They should be as short as possible.
2. Fittings should be reduced to the minimum in order to reduce costs and frictional resistances.
3. All bends should have a large radius and T pieces should have swept branches.

Insulation of Ductwork. Wherever possible, all ductwork should be well insulated. Where there is a danger of the insulation getting wet, e.g. in a solid ground floor, it must be protected by wrapping with

146

Fig. 10.14   Duct under a suspended timber floor.

Fig. 10.15   Duct embedded in concrete floor.

plastic sheeting with taped joints. Heat losses from the building should also be reduced by providing good insulation to the structure. Figs. 10.14 and 10.15 show the methods of installing ductwork underneath a suspended timber ground floor and a solid ground floor respectively.

Sound Emission from Systems

Sound emission from warm air heating systems may be due to mechanical noise, vibration or air turbulence. Mechanical noise may be caused by hum of the electric motor, slack or dry bearings, or an unbalanced fan. Some manufacturers use resiliant mountings to insulate the fan and motor from the structural base. Where ductwork is connected directly to the heater or fan, a soundproof coupling in the form of an insulating rubber gasket or a short length of stout canvas

should be provided. It is also necessary to limit the noise transmission in the vicinity of the heater by enclosing the heater with fireproof acoustic boarding. Noise from air turbulence is not usually a problem with smaller propeller-type fans and is therefore only likely to occur in systems having long lengths of ductwork which require centrifugal or axial flow fans. Noise of this type can be reduced by limiting the angular velocity of the fan and by using bends and fittings which change the direction of the air gradually.

Controls

Controls used in warm air heating systems fall into two groups:

1. controls such as dampers and adjustable grills which control the rate of air flow,

2. controls such as thermostats and time switches which control the air temperature and operating cycles. Thermostatically controlled motorised dampers may also be used. Controls are required to limit both high and low temperatures of air leaving the heater. The low temperature control is necessary to ensure that the fan does not start to circulate the air until it has been warmed up, or cold air will be forced into the rooms causing discomfort to the occupants.

Exercises

1. Describe natural and forced warm air heating systems and state the advantages of each system.
2. Describe direct and indirect warm air heating systems and state the advantages of each system.
3. Sketch an annotated diagram of an indirect warm air heating system for a bungalow.
4. Sketch vertical sections through gas, oil and solid-fuel air heaters and explain their operating principles.
5. Sketch the layout of the ductwork for the following warm air heating systems and state the advantages of each:
   (a) extended plenum,
   (b) radial,
   (c) stepped duct,
   (d) stub duct.
6. Show by means of sketches the method of installing warm air ducts
   (a) below a concrete ground floor,
   (b) below a timber floor.
7. Sketch and explain the operating principles of a modulated air and heat output warm air heating system and state its advantages.
8. Describe how the return air is brought back to the war air heater and also how some fresh air from outside is mixed with the return air.
9. State the materials that can be used for warm air ducts and the precautions which must be taken to reduce air flow resistance through the ductwork.
10. State the possible causes of noise from a warm air heating system and the methods that can be used for its prevention.

Answers to Numerical Exercises

Chapter 1

11. 2.943 mbar, 294.3 Pa

Chapter 5

12. 1500 l, 30 kW
13. 74 mm (use a 76 mm diameter pipe)
14. 9 m (approx.)
15. 16
16. 31.3 (use a 32 mm diameter pipe)

Chapter 8

2. 3.8 W/m² K
3. $U = 0.54$ W/m² K (approx.)
4. 935.6 W (approx.)
5. 2268.5 W and 4.2 m²

Chapter 9

10. 128.5 kPa (approx.)

Index

150